The Narrow Window

Understanding AI and Our Role in Shaping its Future

Wilim Abrook

Edition 1.0, 2024

ISBN: 978-989-33-6764-3

This book is intended to provide general information and is based on the author's research and experiences.

Cover Image: "Electric Discharges" (1909)
Cover Layout Design: Stefan Prodanovic

For Berri,
who listened to every word

And Dad,
who proofed every draft

Table of Contents:

The Sleight Revolution

I am old enough to remember a time before the Internet; those heady days when you would arrange to meet your friend outside the video store after school and if they didn't show up, you'd just... go home.

Back then, if you wanted to know the distance to Azerbaijan, or how much water was in the ocean, you had to accept it as a passing thought and be content in not knowing. Or, if your curiosity really got the better of you, you would go to the local library and seek answers from some dusty tome. So it was fitting then, that when the Information Age dawned in my small town, it did so in the library. You'd sign your name on a waiting list and, a few days later, sit at one of the library's four personal computers and Surf the Web.

It was mostly aimless site-hopping amidst flashing neon banners. I was not instantly awestruck by the weight of all mankind's knowledge pressing out of the screen. It was a novelty, but it was quickly normalised and backgrounded. By the time we got a modem of our very own, screeching and chirping to itself in the corner of the computer room (née Dining Room), it already felt like catching up on a necessity. Essential, but mundane.

In reality, what I was actually witnessing was a revolution more profound than the French, October, or Industrial. There was talk and hype, and opinions abounded, but its swift insinuation into every facet of our lives was by most, and for the most part, unrecognised until it had already happened.

Of course, one could certainly say that many a societal revolution has crept by, taking its contemporaries off guard; but none, I believe, married such subtle normalcy with such disruptive ferocity. We are on the cusp at the moment, depending on how you look at it, of either the crescendo phase of the revolution of my youth, or an entirely new one, either way rendering what preceded as foothills to the peaks of our horizon.[1]

And yet, I see it again; and for closer observation can now make out the patterns perhaps, that allow such

---

[1] Unless we blow ourselves up first.

nonchalance in the face of cataclysmic upheaval. Of course, there's a chorus of doomsayers and lyrical waxers, but most people are focusing on the immediate and the graspable. They're discussing the patterns of ripples, without much thought for the shape rising from beneath, or what might happen when it breaches the surface.

I am reminded of a magician flourishing his wand, drawing away your attention while he performs some sleight of hand. Or perhaps it's better to say simply, we are at risk of missing the forest for the trees.

I've always had an interest in machine intelligence. I've pondered the implications of super-intelligent Banksian Minds with utmost fascination. Now, as I potentially see their coming into being, I'm of course impatient and data-hungry. I want to know what will unfold; why, how, and now! (A product of the age of immediacy.)

As things warmed up in late 2022, I wanted to know how my industry, online language teaching, would be impacted and transformed. I started by searching for "AI in education" and "future of AI in the classroom", and I did find some wonderful talks and articles, temporarily sating my thirst, but these were rather thin on the ground.

So, in my frustration, I turned to the fluff; at first to scorn, then to empathise, and now maybe identifying a space to fill. They usually start off with some varying degree of bravado – videos with clickbait titles, conference speakers with letters after their names, articles proclaiming what you Need To Know[2] – but before too long that phrase pops up, "I'm not an expert in AI, but..." What follows is typically a series of Top Tips from someone who's spent six months tinkering on Chat GPT, and has found some limited practical applications which may or may not replace certain tasks and save you time.

Now, that's my harshest reading of the situation – a reflexive lashing out at not getting what I wanted. But calming down, and with a fairer mind, I see that I should relate very deeply. Here are educators, taking the time to investigate a brand-new tool, and keen to share their newly gleaned insights. It's genuinely helpful to some, just not what I'm after.

So what am I after?

I want to muse on the real future of education, and of every other industry. I want to discuss the opportunities,

---

[2] Also clickbait, usually...

the pitfalls, how our world may evolve, and how we as a society will need to rise up and meet it.

What I really want is medium-level futurism on terms I can relate to, with practical, actionable advice, to help me feel some sense of control in a world that I see spinning towards potentially dangerous escalation.

Rather hypocritically, I can also say that I am not an expert in AI.[3] My field is in education – I can explain things quite well. Another issue I've noticed is the lack of a middle ground. Everything is either fluff, as I've described above, or far too technical. I'm attempting to write for the average person, who wants to learn more about AI's impacts, rather than the basics of using it or how to build it.

My ultimate, lofty objective is to give you a more holistic foundation on what AI is, how significant the socio-economic change we're facing is, and above all to empower you to use that literacy proactively, to advocate for the future you'd like to see, and shape it. You may be an expert

---

[3] Although in the course of researching and writing this book, as well as heading up projects implementing AI tools in virtual classroom software, I now feel I'm getting closer. For now, let's say I'm quite experienced and comfortable with AI.

in your own field, and I'd like every expert to be pitching in and enriching the conversation.

And I'd like to motivate you to do it now, because we have a very narrow window.

The Narrow Window

Let's picture a little girl growing up in China. She hears everything around her. Her little brain is in overdrive. It's a compact, but profoundly complex and powerful pattern recognition machine. She hears certain sounds repeated again and again as her parents speak around her, and so hones in on those sounds. She builds up a coherent library of expected phonemes and patterns, and becomes an expert in plucking those patterns out of the cacophony. After a while she starts emulating them. The first words in most languages actually sound pretty similar – they're some of the easiest to physically create with a human vocal apparatus – in this case, "Māmā."

After a few more years of building and refining her internal phonemic library, something interesting happens; While our little girl has become intuitively proficient at distinguishing between sounds like /t͡ʂ/ and /t͡ʂʰ/[4], she has deprioritised the sounds such as /r/ and /l/, or /ð/ and θ/[5]. The result is that she not only has difficulty pronouncing these sounds – she essentially doesn't hear the difference. They are not in her library for reference. This is why Chinese speakers typically struggle with "light, right, this, thanks", and conversely, why English speakers stumble over "zhī, chī". It's also been the cause of many arguments with my Polish-speaking wife, who insists that /ʐ/ and /ʐ/[6] are different sounds which I should learn to distinguish, whereas I, an anglophone, refuse.

Okay, let's backpedal away from the complicated phonemic symbols and domestic arguments. The important thing here is that our little Chinese girl focussed on the ability to recognise certain sounds, at the expense of others. That's why you may have a very strong accent in a second language according to native speakers, but struggle to hear it yourself. It takes a long time and a

---

[4] zh (ㄓ) and ch, (ㄔ) are similar to the "ch" (/tʃ/) sound in English but with a retroflex articulation. The zh is aspirated and ch is not. These sounds can be extremely difficult for English speakers to pronounce and distinguish.

[5] /ð/ and /θ/ are the voiced and unvoiced "th" sounds in "that" and "thanks".

[6] They sound the same.

lot of conscious effort to retrain your brain so that you can speak, *and hear*, clearly.

Now let's picture our ancestors; ape, mammal, fish, and tiny blob; traversing primordial landscapes. These creatures seldom encountered very big numbers, or phenomena that blossomed exponentially. The world unfolded in a linear progression. When your goals in life are to find a mate, find food, avoid being food, and so on; truly large numbers may come up, but they are quite irrelevant to you. So there's a cognitive dilemma, rooted in our evolutionary blueprint. We have not honed in on certain patterns, which are now missing from our library.

So, like the Chinese or English speakers who struggle to grasp foreign sounds, we find it very difficult to reckon with millions, billions, and exponential growth.

Clear your mind.

Picture a sphere, a little ball.

Now picture another. Maybe they're floating in space, bobbing gently.

Now add two more. Four balls, floating in a little square.

Now skip a few steps. Picture 144 balls.

Focus, and you can do it: A square grid, 12 balls to a side.

Now picture one million balls.

One billion.

A trillion...

These numbers are increasingly societally relevant – maybe even personally relevant, you lucky devil! – but we are simply not equipped to deal with them. The mind's eye lacks the ability to accurately hold that image.[7]

In a world that just witnessed the tumult of a pandemic, one would expect a far better grasp on such things. After all, much of our recent experience was impacted directly by the charts and graphs many of us were glued to on the news every night.

In spite of that, however, most of us still can't coherently picture things like exponential growth. I would argue that it may even be *because of* the charts we saw on the news. I remember an article on Covid-19 cases in Italy, back in the spring of 2020, when things really got frightening. I couldn't understand why the line I was looking at seemed to be stabilising, while the article expounded uncontrollable infection rates. Then it hit me, I was looking at a logarithmic chart, not a linear one. So for every one step on the y-axis, the cases were increasing tenfold.

---

[7] For your reference, a million seconds is 12 days. A billion seconds is 31 years.

In the image below, fig.1(a) shows steady growth on a linear chart, and fig.1(b) depicts the exact same data logarithmically. You can see that both trend lines end at the same value, 100, but fig.1(b) *seems* much less severe. It's easy to get the impression that growth was strong at first, but then quickly fell off.

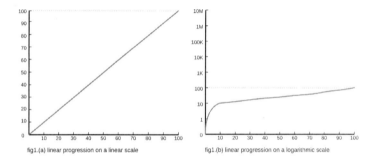

fig1.(a) linear progression on a linear scale   fig1.(b) linear progression on a logarithmic scale

This is exactly what happened during the pandemic, compounded by the fact that the duration of the crisis normalised it. "The new normal" was the catchword at the time. In fig.2, opposite, we again see linear and logarithmic depictions, this time of global Covid-19 cases. In the last three months, the total number suddenly doubled, but in fig.2(b) you can barely make out a blip on the trendline.

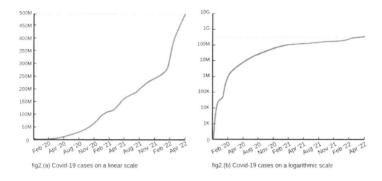

fig2.(a) Covid-19 cases on a linear scale   fig2.(b) Covid-19 cases on a logarithmic scale

The most common allegory to help visualise exponentials is the pond and the lily pad. Each day, the lily pad doubles in size. On the twentieth day, it covers the whole pond. On which day was the pond half-covered? The answer is not the tenth day, but the nineteenth. The problem seemed small and unassuming, until suddenly it wasn't.

This difficulty in grasping exponential growth is not just a result of unfamiliarity. Experts who regularly have to tackle exponentials, in fields such as artificial intelligence or climate change, have also been shown to wildly underestimate the speed at which certain milestones will be met. These are people who are dealing with the data every day, and still, the sheer inertia of the phenomena they're investigating is not always apparent. I would tentatively chalk this up to biology – the patterns our brains have evolved to pick up on, or in this case, those they haven't.

Artificial Intelligence (AI) is set to have an exponential influence on our society, driven by a confluence of factors. Of course, the reality is extremely complicated, but for the sake of brevity, let's be reductive:

1. Rapid Technological Evolution: The technology underpinning AI is advancing at a breakneck pace. Not only are AI systems becoming more sophisticated, but advancements in different fields of AI, which were previously quite separated, are starting to be more easily cross-applicable. There's also the elephant in the room, which people won't stop mentioning – AI can potentially be employed to design even more advanced AI. This is often presented as a doomsday scenario, so be mindful of the hype, but there are certain specific dangers and concerns to bear in mind.

2. Acceleration of Societal Adoption: As AI tools continue their foray into various facets of our lives,

the initial hesitancy and novelty surrounding them begins to dissipate. The rate of AI adoption thus starts increasing, mirroring exponential growth patterns.

3. Broad Application Spectrum: AI isn't one limited, specialised tool. Its potential applications span across every single domain, from finance to farming, housing to healthcare. As AI permeates these diverse sectors, its impacts start interplaying, leading to a compounded effect. It's crucial to realise that the introduction of AI isn't analogous to introducing a singular tool like a hammer. It's more like introducing the *concept* of tools – a paradigm shift that redefines how tasks are approached and accomplished.

In essence, the exponential growth and influence of AI are not just products of its technological prowess but also of its ever-expanding applications and our evolving relationship with it. As we continue to weave AI into the fabric of our society, its impact will be amplified in ways we are only beginning to comprehend.

We are now at the start of that journey. Historically, it may seem like a brilliant flash, after which nothing was ever the same. For those of us here and now, riding the wave, it could be wildly disruptive and even destructive.

I'm not saying we ought to stop it – it essentially can't be stopped at this point, the tech is out of the bag – but we really need to tread carefully. The attention-grabbing, reaction-provoking dangers of AI are real, but the benefits likely dwarf the risks. Possibly within our lifetimes, things are going to change utterly. And we're uniquely placed to influence that future.

That's what the "Narrow Window" is. We're perched on the edge of the abyss, and the time we have to plan our leap, and check our parachutes, is running out.

An Electric Tablecloth

So that's it, then? A tidal wave is rearing up above us, and there's naught we can do with these last few seconds but curl into the brace position?

Well, not quite.

Like most things in life, the reality isn't so binary. We do have an unfortunate tendency these days to strip out the nuance and plunge straight towards the most attention-grabbing aspects of things.[8]

When hearing about the exponential growth of AI technology, we'd do well to bear in mind who is waving the flag and what they have to gain from doing so. Industry experts, being experts, obviously, should have a bit more weight given to their words. But remember that, in many cases, they could be drawing profit from the hype

---

8 Acknowledging that much of what I've just written can be said to have participated in that exact practice.

– in the form of publicity, public opinion, and ultimately investment in their firms. The same goes for people like me, who are trying to drum up attention, interest, and even that crucial spark of fear in order to sell books, talks, and workshops.

So is it all fluff and nonsense, then?

Of course not!

Now we're back to that binary attitude. The truth lies somewhere in the middle. But there are two important assertions from the previous section that I'll stand by:

1. The technology truly has the *capacity* to grow at an exponential rate. While it's important here to consider the real–world challenges that could slow AI's practical adoption, its abilities do seem to be improving at a faster rate than many linear models would predict.

2. This really is different from everything we've seen before. Making a direct comparison to previous technological leaps runs the risk of downplaying the magnitude of what's before us. It's easy to fall into that old trap of "It worked

out fine before, I don't see why this should be any different."

That's not to say, however, that we won't be able to glean some insights and draw interesting parallels from the past to prepare ourselves for the future.

The late 18th and early 19th centuries marked an era of electrifying discoveries,[9] both literally and figuratively, as society grappled with the new wonders of electricity. It wouldn't be until the 1870s, and the development of commercially viable lightbulbs by Edison and Swan that domestic electricity really caught on. From the 1880s, cities in the United States and Europe began extensive electrification projects. Just a few decades later, it had become an essential utility in every home and business.

That's not to say it was a smooth ride, bringing a brand-new technology to millions of users, unfamiliar with its workings and ignorant to its dangers. The public were totally unprepared to deal with the electrified home. Poorly insulated or even uninsulated wires were run along wooden fixings; People plugged multiple appliances into a

---

° I'm sorry. There were too many puns for me to resist.

single lightning socket; Fuses or circuit breakers had yet to be introduced, so when the inevitable fire started and water was poured or sprayed into the room, the electricity kept flowing.

Another symptom of a totally uncomprehending public was how they embraced ineffective and occasionally reckless misapplications. An oft-cited example of the naïve enthusiasm of the age was Henry Cooper's electric tablecloth. Rather than running unsightly wires across the table, Cooper's contraption allowed the modern dinner host to plug light fittings directly into live elements – copper strips running through the fabric. Fantastic and convenient, until the first person spills their drink and sets the house on fire.

In Cooper's case, we can reasonably assume there was no malicious intent in the endangerment of his few customers.[10] We can't say the same for every inventor, however. Where we may see a public that is naïve and ill-informed, others may see gullible marks, ripe for the conning. Englishman Dr. George Scott, a peddler of electrical quackery in 1880s America, patented several "electrical" inventions such as hairbrushes, insoles, and

---

[10] The electric tablecloth, thankfully, never found legs.

corsets. These devices, unlike Cooper's tablecloth, had no electric current flowing through them, but rather had magnets embedded somewhere in the product, allowing Scott to claim that the marvellous electromagnetic field did wonders for all sorts of ailments – from lameness and rheumatism to hair loss, diseases of the blood, or even paralysis.

While such claims now seem outlandish – and would even have seemed so to many at the time – there was so much hype around electricity that the public couldn't get enough of this fantastic miracle technology, which could seemingly do everything and anything. Another thing that points towards Scott's purposeful manipulation of public interest is the warning printed on the hairbrush packaging:

"In no case should more than one person use the brush. If always used by the same person, it retains its full curative power."

While it's difficult to imagine any practical reason that the power of the magic hairbrush would be diminished by sharing, it's very easy to see why Scott would want each member of a household to purchase their own.

At the very end of the 19th century, the discovery of radium by Marie Skłodowska-Curie spurred a similar frenzy known as the Radium Rush. Again we see a new and alluring technology capturing the public imagination. The mysterious glow was irrationally equated with healthful properties and this saw radium being infused into a plethora of products, from toothpaste, which promised a radiant smile at the potential cost of disintegrating jaws, to health tonics like Radithor that guaranteed vigour but delivered lethal radiation poisoning. These products were not only a public health disaster but also a stark manifestation of the dangers of unchecked technological enthusiasm.

That era's technological adolescence was marked by a sociological phenomenon of trial and error, with society at large acting as the laboratory. The misuse of electricity in everyday items like the electric tablecloth, and the hazardous inclusion of radium in consumer products, mirrored a broader societal trend: a fascination with the new and novel, often overshadowing prudent caution. These early missteps in handling new technologies were characterised by an optimistic disregard for potential dangers, driven by a cultural and economic push for innovation and modernisation.

But of course, we've moved on since then, and would never allow the unchecked dissemination of a potentially dangerous new technology into society without rigorous and effective safety regulation. Right?

As we look more closely at technological innovations throughout recent history, an interesting pattern emerges. The "Hype Cycle," is a concept developed by American research and technology advisory firm Gartner. It provides a useful reference framework to understand the adoption, maturity, and social application of new technologies. The cycle comprises five dramatically named phases:

1. The Technology Trigger
    This refers to the introduction of the new tech into society, rather than its initial invention or discovery. For AI, we can quite firmly place this in November 2022 with the public release of ChatGPT.

2. The Peak of Inflated Expectations
    Early publicity produces a number of success stories, and the hype begins. This period is marked by ambitious projects and a surge in investment, with companies promoting their

products as revolutionary. Although it seems quite brief on the chart, we could say that this period for AI extends well into 2024, with just the first signs emerging of AI-fatigue, bringing us into the next stage.

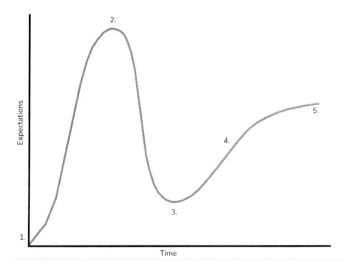

3. The Trough of Disillusionment

Dubious applications proliferate, often over-shadowing appropriate and effective uses. As the hype wanes, these impractical applications become more visible and apparent. Carelessly over-confident promises fail to provide fruition, leading to public disenchantment and a lack of trust in the technology.

4. The Slope of Enlightenment
    The subsequent phase is where we begin to see a more balanced and informed application of the technology. It is during this phase that the public and industries start to understand more deeply its practical benefits and limitations, adjusting their expectations accordingly

5. The Plateau of Productivity
    Finally we come to the Plateau of Productivity, where the technology's true and sustainable value is realised and integrated into everyday life.

Understanding the Gartner curve is useful for resolving the perceived disparity between what's touted and what we experience. However, it's worth remembering that this curve charts public opinion rather than the capacity of the technology itself. That continues to grow at a ferocious rate, whether we feel AI-fatigued or not.

However, the assumption that this ferocity will continue unchecked overlooks the significant physical, regulatory, and social barriers that inherently stifle such advancement. It's essential to distinguish between the *potential* growth and the practical limitations that temper it.

One of the most formidable physical barriers to AI's exponential trajectory relates to its substantial energy demands. The data centres used to train and operate these models consume enormous and increasing amounts of electricity. For instance, while GPT-3 took 1.3 gigawatt-hours of energy to train, GPT-4 required 50 times more. As AI becomes more widespread across various industries, this energy demand will continue to rise.

Data centres are now a major contributor to our global carbon emissions. They currently account for 3% of global electricity use, producing as much CO_2 as all of Brazil. This energy demand is only expected to increase. In the United States alone, the power demand driven by data centres is expected to represent 6% of the nation's total power usage by 2026.

Something many people don't realise about data centres is that they also use a lot of water. All those computer servers whirring away generate a lot of heat, and have to be cooled down. A single conversation on ChatGPT can require the equivalent of a whole bottle of water.

What's more, we can no longer rely on Moore's Law to save us. Moore's Law, named after Gordon Moore, co-founder of Intel, originated from his observation in a 1965 paper; Moore noted that the number of transistors on a microchip doubles approximately every two years, as the cost of computers is halved. This observation has held true for decades, predicting advances in computing power, miniaturisation, and cost reduction in electronics.

Moore's Law is often understood as a prediction that computing power will increase exponentially forever, as more transistors are packed into silicon chips. Smaller, more powerful computers would mean smaller, more energy efficient data centres, but there is strong evidence that Moore's Law might be reaching its limits. Even as the number of transistors continues to rise, the speed improvements from new chip generations have plateaued. This is because the benefits of smaller transistors are offset by the challenges of power management and heat dissipation. This has led to changes in chip design, such as adding more processor cores rather than just increasing transistor density and clock speed.

More interesting, as transistors shrink to atomic sizes, we encounter quantum and thermodynamic limits. These include issues like quantum tunnelling, where electrons leak across thin barriers; and heat dissipation problems, as packing more transistors into a chip leads to greater power density and heat generation. These problems complicate further miniaturisation and efficiency improvements.[11]

Without the ability to pack more computing power into the same chip size due to physical and economic constraints, data centres may need to accommodate more hardware to meet growing computational demands. This could lead to much larger physical footprints. Their overall energy consumption is also likely to increase. This challenges the sustainability goals of many organisations, especially those pledged to carbon neutrality or reduced environmental footprints, which so often amount to lip-service greenwashing.

Another big issue is data – the raw material we use to create AI models. Once we've trained AI with all available data online, how do we get more data that's suitable?

---

[11] While quantum computers are an exciting new technology on our horizon, they aren't the answer to the quantum effects we're encountering here. Although they could constitute a massive leap in processing power, we're nowhere near that point just yet.

According to Open AI's Leopold Aschenbrenner, the solution is simple – robots. But where do these robots come from? Aschenbrenner posits that advancements in AI will resolve any remaining challenges in robotics, allowing the first wave of robots to establish factories capable of producing more robots. So we make robots to mine the materials and build the factories for more robots, who then go out into the world in swarms and collect the data needed to train AI models in data centres, each one requiring their own massive energy infrastructure just to run.

If this sounds a little far-fetched to you, you're not alone. Leaving aside the wild socio-economic and environmental impacts, the main problem is that navigating the regulations and industrial restrictions required for such an undertaking would be a colossal task.

Regulatory barriers directly imposed on AI technology will also play a critical role in shaping its adoption curve. As AI technologies become more pervasive, governments worldwide are stepping up to implement stringent regulations aimed at protecting data privacy and preventing ethical abuses. These regulations, while necessary for safeguarding social interests, also act as speed bumps, slowing the rapid deployment of AI solutions and ensuring they align with broader human values.

The neo-liberal view is, as always, that regulation impedes innovation and will do more harm than good. My viewpoint comes at it from a different angle. Regulation impedes profit, but is essential in imbuing protections into society. However, with tech giants exerting more and more influence, and their enigmatic leaders acting more like oligarchs, one worrying outcome would be regulation that doesn't fully protect us from the big players, but still stifles innovation by hampering the smaller players.

How and when regulation gets implemented is strongly impacted of course by public perception. Social barriers arising from the societal impact of AI may significantly influence its acceptance and integration. The fear of job displacement due to automation, the potential for misuse of AI in scams and porn, and the overall erosion of trust in digital systems could lead to public backlash, with populist governments enacting reactionary prohibitions, which would inevitably be ineffective, but could stunt development both of the technology itself, and of our ability to wield it.

And it's that *wielding* we should be focusing on. Of course, the tech behind domestic electricity improved dramatically between the 1880s and the 1930s, but most of the problems we mentioned earlier were not due to the technology itself but to our incompetence and ignorance – or, to be kinder, our unfamiliarity with how to effectively implement it.

When discussing the growth of AI, there are three distinct yet interconnected trajectories to consider: the capacity of the technology itself, its adoption, and its application.

The Capacity Curve

What can it actually do?

The technology growth curve of AI traces the evolution from rudimentary algorithms to sophisticated systems capable of learning and adapting. While there are periods of rapid innovation, these are typically followed by phases of slower, more incremental improvements. Each technological leap forwards builds on previous advancements, setting the stage for the next set of innovations.

However, all the amazing advancements and ideas in the world aren't worth a thing unless we put them into practice.

The Adoption Curve

How broadly is it being implemented?

It's well known that the adoption of AI has been increasing at a blistering pace.

ChatGPT is estimated to have reached 100 million monthly active users in just two months, making it the fastest-growing consumer application in history. However, we shouldn't conflate the number of ChatGPT users with the broader adoption of AI. Unlike social media platforms, which can saturate their market once a critical mass of users is reached, AI's potential applications span a far broader spectrum. There is a lot more than just ChatGPT, a lot more than large language models. From healthcare to automotive industries, the adoption of AI is only just beginning to make its transformative impacts felt.

Moreover, the adoption of AI is not a uniform process; it varies significantly by sector, region, and application. Each industry has its own set of challenges and rates of adoption, influenced by factors such as regulatory environments, technological readiness, and market demand. As AI continues to evolve, its adoption will likely penetrate deeper into various sectors, driven by a clear demonstration of its value and utility.

If we were to halt the capacity curve so that the technology remains the same as it is today, the adoption curve would still continue to rise, and with it, the impact that AI has on our world.

The Application Curve

How good are we at using it?

Finally, we have the application curve, which measures the efficacy of our implementation, its actual impact. Right now, we're in the very early stages of understanding how to use AI and where it fits into our workflows and processes.

Think of the time difference between accidentally electrocuting your dinner guests because you ran wires through a tablecloth, and the emergence of complex circuitry and electronics just a few decades later.

So, once again, even if the technology itself remains unchanged, its impact would continue to expand at a tremendous rate. One of the most significant effects it's predicted to have is on employment – if AI can be leveraged to perform so much work, where does that leave us?

Becoming Redundant

It has been said that AI will do for humans what the industrial revolution did for horses. Wassily Leontief, a Nobel Laureate economist, discussed this in 1982:

> *"[Horses] became unnecessary with the advent of tractors, automobiles and trucks. And a farmer couldn't keep his horses and postpone the change to tractors by feeding them less oats. So he got rid of the horses and used the more productive tractor. After all, this doesn't precipitate a political problem, since horses don't vote"*

Of course, automation taking the roles of human workers is something we're all familiar with. The archetype is the factory worker displaced by machines or robots. Our experience, however, tells us that although these displacements are inevitable, the progress and increased productivity ultimately heralds prosperity for all. Living standards are raised, people are healthier, richer, and happier. The luddites standing stubbornly in the way of mankind's betterment are eventually debunked and forgotten.

As before, so again, right?

Let's look at the automatic teller machine, a device we're all familiar with. When ATMs were introduced in the 1970s, they were initially perceived as a threat to employment, with many assuming it would reduce the need for human tellers. However, contrary to these assumptions, the presence of ATMs did not lead to a decrease in teller employment. Instead, the number of teller jobs has continued to grow steadily, even outpacing the growth of the general labour force.

The introduction of ATMs reduced the number of tellers required per bank branch, making it more economical to operate one. As a consequence, banks were motivated to open more branch offices, leading to an increased demand for tellers. The role of bank tellers also evolved; while cash-handling became less vital, interpersonal and marketing skills grew in importance. This transition elevated the bank teller's role, aligning them more with a bank's customer relationship team. Additionally, the skills required for the role became more specialised, leading to higher wages and a trend towards hiring more educated individuals for these positions.

So fewer workers per branch, but more branches, meaning more workers overall. But bank branches had been less numerous, so there was space to open more. This isn't the same for all markets. Grocery and retail stores, for example, are already very common, so we can't expect self-checkout systems to result in more and more shops.

Self-checkout machines have gained a lot of traction over the past decade. It's now increasingly common to see them even in small corner shops. Many businesses implement them to offset hiring challenges, especially as the industry has high employee turnover. A machine won't quit or complain about long shifts.

A 2019 report by the think tank New America highlighted retail workers' aversion to self-checkout machines, viewing them as a means to reduce hours and eliminate positions. The report also emphasised the need for stronger worker representation and improved labour laws.

Again, the number of cashier positions overall has grown since 2010. However, the U.S. Bureau of Labor Statistics now projects a 10% decline in cashier employment from

2022 to 2032, driven by technological advances and a shift to online sales. It predicts that although there will be some job openings, "almost *all* of those openings are expected to result from the need to replace workers who transfer to other occupations or exit the labor force."

What about the nature of the job itself? We saw that the role of bank tellers evolved into a more highly-paid and respected customer relationship specialist. In retail, for those of you who haven't graced the tills, customer service isn't always a barrel of laughs. When self-checkouts were first introduced, customers simply did not like them. In fact, many articles dispelling fears of mass redundancy wave this red herring around, like a fishy battle flag.

But people are always resistant to change at first, and technologies are always a bit clunky, at first. So the role of cashier evolved to that of a troubleshooter and thief stopper. Their interaction with customers is now full of frustration and suspicion. The work is often underpaid, underappreciated, and overwhelming. This compounds the high staff turnover, and management seem even less motivated to improve working conditions. I remember when my local supermarket first introduced these machines. The familiar friendly face of Mary, a cashier I had brief interactions with most days, became drawn and weary, as she was made to stand for her entire shift, expected to hawkishly watch for sticky fingers, intervene when people got angry with her new-fangled replacement, and teach them how better to replace her.

Even bank tellers aren't really safe. Projections indicate that the number of teller positions will decline by 15% in the coming decade due to industry consolidation and advancements in technology. It turns out that ATMs weren't the sole driver behind the flurry of branch openings. They were one factor, in a complex web of context and happenstance. Now that market has changed again, and branches are closing. We will still likely have more banks than in the 80s, but we won't have more tellers.

Maybe I'm falling into the same narrow trap here – the bank teller and supermarket cashier aren't limited to just those roles, they can find work elsewhere (unlike the machines that ousted them). While the Bureau of Labor Statistics predicts double figure declines for those specific positions, the overall job market is expected to rise by three percent over the same period. Perhaps the AI doomsayers, warning of mass unemployment, are the luddites of our age. Perhaps.

In 1811, Ned Ludd[12] led a band of textile workers, terrified that newly-invented knitting machines would ruin their livelihoods. They used force, smashing machinery and attacking owners, and were considered to be small-minded opposers of civilised progress. The term "luddite" has taken that meaning to this day, someone who ignorantly rejects new ways of working.

The full story of the Luddite movement though, struggling against a harsh economic reality, and ultimately put down by military intervention, is more complex and multi-faceted. The best summation I've read, from Eric Hobsbawm in 1952, is "collective bargaining by riot".

The Luddites were not afraid that human labour would be replaced totally. They were protesting the shift from expert craftspeople, who had trained and invested extensively in their vocations, to unskilled machinery operators – in a world before worker protection legislation. After years, even decades of dedicated service, you could be turfed out unceremoniously, with no way to

---

[12] Likely apocryphal, but narratively satisfying

provide for yourself or your family. Ending up in the workhouse was the stuff of nightmares, enough to set reasonable men on a violent course. The idea that the lower classes might not do as they're told, however, was the stuff of nightmares for the powers-that-be, enough to set an army twelve thousand strong on their own people, more than they'd fielded against the French army at Alexandria ten years before.

Equating the word "luddite" with unschooled obstructionism is the result of, as writer E. P. Thompson once put it "the enormous condescension of posterity". We should really be looking at that movement in the same way people look at the Boston Tea Party, an act of rebellion, met with far more violence than it gave out, ultimately resulting in a better world for us, hundreds of years later. Much though an effort is being made to dismantle it, many of us live in a world of labour protection. When AI comes for your job – and it will – you'll want to have that protection. But thinking again of how poorly people grasp the scales involved, I fear that our current legislation simply isn't up to the task. It wasn't designed for it. Because the ATM and the self-checkout kiosk are use-specific, while artificial intelligence isn't as limited at all in its applications. Was that concept considered in the three percent growth the Bureau predicted?

When people talked about AI replacing jobs in the past, they often broke roles and industries down according to their varying levels of risk. Paper pushers and bean counters were up at the front, management and strategists reasonably safe, and creatives and artists essentially untouchable. As a fine art student, I found this stridently reassuring.

However, it seems that we've fallen prey to an age-old problem, essentially rooted in deifying others to mollify ourselves. When we look at great feats of human ingenuity in history, particularly those of peoples our society considers below us,[13] we often downplay or misattribute them. This results in such ludicrous suggestions as the pyramids of Egypt or the Incan Empire having been built by aliens. Surely these ancient savages couldn't have accomplished such feats by themselves?!

It's not always consciously racially motivated (although the hallmarks of racism and colonialism are undeniable here). It can also be borne of a desire to raise ourselves up,

---

[13] In the West, this unfortunately means "anyone browner than us".

to conflate societal and technological advancement with a kind of intellectual superiority. It was in this way that my high school art teacher once commented that classical sculpture was astonishing, since the Romans were "basically cavemen".

This is the same mechanism that has us steal the credit away from artists great and small, and attribute it to the divine. Artists themselves will often talk of a wave of inspiration coursing through them. They speak as if there's some force, bigger than they are; and they are merely a conduit. It can feel that way too, but the reality is that the spark, the burning charge of creation, is coming from within. If, however, we insist on true creativity requiring a preternatural connection to the muses, then machines surely could never replicate it.

But it doesn't, so they can.

As cashiers and tellers are replaceable, so are writers, illustrators, and composers.

It is tempting to look at AI as just another tool, something to enhance, assist, but not replace. From this perspective, my assertions are just as hysterical as that insistence on extra-terrestrial intervention. We've seen again and again, cases where one might think technology is going to destroy jobs but the reverse is true. When barcode scanners were introduced in supermarkets, cashiers weren't replaced, their lives were made easier. When word processors were introduced with auto spell-checkers and easy formatting, the role of the editor didn't die out, it grew. When Apple brought out the Apple Pencil, it made the lives of illustrators much easier.[14] On your iPad, you now have a multitude of tools, all rolled into one, able to reproduce the touch and feel of pens and brushes, and allowing you to be more productive, more free in your creativity.

But none of that is artificial intelligence. AI does not replace the tool in your hand, it replaces the thoughts in your head. It replaces *you*, directly. Even after a thousand-word run up, that statement seems absurd and alarmist, doesn't it?

Let's take a step back, and try to view the bigger picture. Think not of the individual, because by switching that protagonist around, you can always find an exception. Think of industries as we have them now; complicated interconnected social mechanisms, churning out product-

---

[14] Not intentionally advertising here – I distrust Apple as a company, enjoy the pencil as a product.

-ivity and drawing in the time, work, and the ideas of thousands, millions of people. The ultimate driving force is profit. In our modern society, industries follow the money. But the net result is fulfilment, employment, empowerment, and disimpoverishment. This is the beautiful simplicity of capitalism. One common goal, one rooting force, producing a variety of desired outcomes.[15]

This isn't without its flaws of course. What happens when you find an alternative route to the end goal? The system powers on, while the side effects on which we've been relying peter away.

Take the humble illustrator. AI generated artwork can do what the illustrator takes hours and hours to produce. It's currently a fairly blunt and flailing tool, but it's getting better all the time (remember here the exponential curves). AI can't do *everything* a good illustrator can do, but it can do a lot.

Now stop thinking on the individual scale, stop thinking of exceptions and swapping out the illustrator in your mind's eye for another one, more specialised and

---

[15] Yes, yes, I mentioned capitalism but no, I'm not suggesting communism. Nor am I blind to the ravages of unregulated mass consumerism on society and climate at large. Like it or not, capitalism is what our global economy is currently built on.

impervious. Zoom out to consider the whole industry, and everything it touches. Until recently, almost every image you see was *designed*. It was thought about, worked on, and created by a human mind. Every icon, every logo, every wonderfully obnoxious 80s hair metal album cover, every storyboard, every children's picture book, every sign on the bathroom door, the curve and line of every letter on this page, was designed and thought up. Some was done for fun, some for profit, some was done to practise and hone abilities. We can break them into two crude categories: value generators and stepping stones.

Value generators are essentially sources of income. Someone got paid to do this creative work, however much or little. View them as a vast upside-down field of hanging grapes.

Stepping stones are ways to reach those grapes. From an hour of practice or experience to a university degree, they are all stacked into a dazzlingly complex landscape of stairs and rampways, flocked with human workers of all sorts, merrily plucking the grapes from above.

So we've got a surreal landscape, as if Escher imagined a utopia for Tantalus.

Now introduce flocks and flocks of grape-eating birds; faster and more efficient than we are at gobbling up the fruit we so depend on.

Now, as more and more birds are introduced, more and more stepping stones start to disappear, resulting in increasingly inaccessible levels, with widening, gaping divides.

Of course, there are still ways for some people to reach the grapes, and the overall grape consumption goes up, but it's clear enough that the effect amongst the humans is devastating.

Can It Write My Emails Then?

It's around this point that people, who have been nodding along with me, will steeple their fingers and say something like, "I see what you're saying. So, could Chat GPT write an email for me?"

More than once, I've been sitting awe-struck, considering the implications of a presentation I've just heard, and found myself utterly confounded by the questions that people are asking, or rather the lack of comprehension those questions belie.

I do sound terribly condescending there, I know, but the people I've heard asking these seemingly stupid questions were by no means stupid themselves. A problem I've come to recognise is that there's a roadblock for most people when faced with a lot of intimidating jargon. There's a lack of literacy and understanding around AI terms and concepts, which is getting in the way, and clouding people's abilities to think about the bigger picture.

And it can be very intimidating, especially for someone who's not super confident with technology. However, while we don't all need to be AI experts, if it's to weather this transition well, the world does need all of our expertise in the fields in which we do have confidence. I'd like to draw back the curtain, so that you can muse on what's actually important, instead of feeling befuddled about tokens, LLMs, NLP, and XYZABCDs.

In this chapter, we'll take a look at some key terms, and try to provide a base upon which you can be more comfortable discussing AI applications and impacts in a broader sense.

Intelligence

Before we go rushing into AI, or even HI, we need to pause to think about I. As a truly fundamental concept, it's one that merits at least a cursory examination.

Intelligence is the ability to think; to reason (apply logic), and understand (derive context or meaning).

When we try to break this down further, things get terribly fuzzy.

A simple indicator is that intelligence adapts. As Stanford professor Christopher Manning put it, "a fully pre-programmed factory robot is flexible, accurate, and consistent, but not intelligent." It's simply carrying out instructions, not analysing and processing information.

Imagine we give the robot the ability to respond to certain stimuli. It can operate on a simple "if, then" logic, so its movements are impacted by what it "senses" around it. For example, it might treat different objects in different ways, or stop moving if a person enters the room. It's still pre-programmed, but now that it can respond to its environment, is it intelligent?

Maybe not with only a limited list of set responses to choose from, but at what level of complexity would we be able to say it's breached the threshold?

These are fantastic questions if you want to start a fight amongst neuroscientists, philosophers, psychologists, or increasingly, computer scientists.

Without agreement on what intelligence actually *is*, it's almost impossible to measure. What we can measure is breadth of knowledge and performance at tasks. Like a subatomic particle; intelligence cannot be observed directly; we know it's there because we can see its effects. Unlike a particle isolated in lab conditions though, intelligent actors (like humans, mayflies, and artificial thinking engines) exist in a complex world of context and dynamic social interaction. So trying to pin down universal indicators tends to throw up problems around bias, and we always seem to overlook some intelligent capacity or other. As Einstein is famously credited with saying, "If you judge a fish by its ability to climb a tree, it will live its whole life believing that it is stupid."

The most commonly accepted measure of intelligence is one's Intelligence Quotient. IQ tests have been around for over a century now. While popular though, they have significant limitations as comprehensive measures of intelligence. They often focus narrowly on logical reasoning, mathematical skills, and language proficiency, neglecting other important facets like emotional, creative, and practical intelligence. Additionally, studies have shown that IQ tests can be culturally biased, disadvantaging those from different cultural or socio-economic backgrounds due to language and contextual differences.

The important point to take away here is that we currently have little consensus on an actual definition of intelligence. What we can agree on tends to be broad and vague. As psychologist Robert J. Sternberg put it at the turn of the millennium, "Looked at in one way, everyone knows what intelligence is; looked at in another way, no one does."

Artificial Intelligence (AI)

The term "Artificial Intelligence" was coined by another Stanford Professor, John McCarthy, in 1955. He called it "the science and engineering of making intelligent machines".

Really though, we should go back to the father of modern computing, Alan Turing. While Turing didn't specifically use the term AI, his work laid foundational concepts for the field. In his famous 1950 paper, Computing Machinery and Int-elligence, Turing discussed the concept of a machine's ability to exhibit intelligent behaviour equivalent to, or indistinguishable from, that of a human. This idea was later developed into what's known as the Turing Test. The test involves a human evaluator who engages in a natural conversation with one human and one machine, both of whom try to appear human. If the evaluator cannot reliably identify the human, the machine is considered to have passed the test.

The Turing Test doesn't evaluate the computer's ability to give correct answers to questions, only how closely its responses *resemble* those a human might give. The big problem with the Turing Test is that it's not really looking at a machine's general intelligence; it's testing its ability to dupe a human. If passing this test is our principal benchmark for developing AI models, they'll tend to find a way of cheating, essentially just breaking the test by finding ways around it, rather than achieving the result (general intelligence) that we're aiming for.

This is the issue with benchmarks and proxies. Since we don't have one coherent definition of intelligence, we cannot have a coherent definition of *artificial* intelligence. Google's François Chollet attempted to address this in his 2019 paper, On the Measure of Intelligence. Chollet was looking for a new way to test intelligence, smoothing out some of the disparities in our definitions and, with his new framework, the Abstraction and Reasoning Corpus (ARC), reorient AI developers towards a more effective goal. The ARC and systems like it are a great practical tool in furthering the field, but even these most modern ideas aren't really providing a coherent definition for us. They're just dealing with the problem of benchmark biases by acknowledging, even embracing them, and using them to nudge things in a more desirable direction. Uncontrolled bias skews results in uncontrolled ways. control the bias and you can influence the results.

So we can see that experts in the field are grappling with the ambiguity around measuring and defining AI. What about a simpler, more practical definition?

Marvin Minsky, another giant in AI research, once described it as "the science of making machines capable of performing tasks that would require intelligence if done by humans."

So here we're looking at the simulation of *human* capabilities, specifically related to tasks. By this definition, could a calculator be considered a simple form of AI?

It's just repeating the same pre-programmed action but it takes an input, and then needs to do some "thinking", or at least does work that would require a human to think in order to complete.

I think what most of us imagine about when we hear the term AI is some form of autonomous system, one which can decide *how* to accomplish a goal, so in that sense, the calculator isn't intelligent, since its *methodology* is pre-set.

Machine Learning

Machine Learning is a subset of AI in which computers are trained to learn from data, identify patterns, and make decisions with minimal human intervention. Unlike traditional programming, where humans explicitly code the desired behaviour, machine learning enables the system to learn and improve from experience. In old text-based adventure games, the computer could spin a narrative depending on your choices and inputs. However, every word of that narrative was programmed, preset, prewritten, so it wasn't generating the story itself, just choosing which path to follow. With machine learning, we provide the start and end points and allow the machine to find its own path.

There are many different approaches to machine learning, drawing from fields like psychology, neuroscience, statistics, and economics.

Much of the AI in use today has been developed using supervised learning, where the computer is trained on a tagged dataset, and essentially becomes a really good sorting and labelling machine. Think about spam detection, medical diagnostics, image classification, and speech recognition.

The most successful approach in machine learning to date has been Deep Learning.

Deep Learning & Neural Networks

When people hear these terms, there's a tendency to feel overly impressed or intimidated. In reality they can be easy enough concepts to grasp.

A neural network is an architecture, a way of structuring a machine learning process, which is inspired by the connections between neurons in a biological brain. However, it's actually quite a simplified version. Each node or "neuron" in our network is connected to a number of others. Think about it like a flowchart. At every step, you need to make a decision, process one little aspect of the information in order to pass on to the next step.[16]

The really powerful thing about neural networks is that the power doesn't come just from the number of nodes you have. It arises from how they are interconnected and layered. This complexity allows the network to learn and model intricate patterns in data, which is key to its power in machine learning tasks. In a human brain, a one kilo lump of mostly

---

[16] The processing at each node involves a combination of weighted inputs, a bias term, and usually a non-linear activation function, which are not just binary decisions (1/0, Yes/No) but more complex mathematical operations. In brief - a number value goes in, and depending on how big it is, it's altered and passed on the the next node.

fat and water, there are 100 billion neurons, but over 100 trillion synaptic connections. That's more connections than there are stars *and planets* in the whole galaxy, in something that could fit in your hands.[17]

Deep learning doesn't mean a depth of under-standing or mastery over a topic. The "deep" just refers to how many layers of steps you have. How deep does the flowchart go before coming to a decision? In a typical neural network, you might expect tens or hundreds of layers.

What's really interesting about deep learning is that the code is not written so much as "grown", allowed to develop on its own.

Open AI's Andrej Karpathy described this as "Software 2.0" – not just another tool or technique, but a fundamental shift in how software is developed.

---

[17] Or head.

Generative AI

Generative AI simply refers to an AI tool that *generates* something new, based on user input. This could be any form of data or media created by the AI, but we mostly think of images, video, audio, and of course, text.

Large Language Models

Now we get to models like ChatGPT, Gemini, Claude, and other tools you may already be familiar with. These are like the grand libraries of the neural network world, specialised in processing human language.[18] Although the AI revolution was under way well before 2023, LLMs were what exploded it into the public consciousness.

LLMs are trained on enormous datasets comprising a wide array of textual information – from classic literature to essays to snippets of text from popup ads. Worryingly, a lot of this training data was just

---

[18] It's worth bearing in mind here that language is how we describe and express *everything*, so mastery of language is very powerful stuff indeed.

scrubbed from the internet. The text is fed into the LLM, which learns to identify patterns in the language: how words form sentences, what responses and continuations can be expected, and how to predict what might logically come next in a piece of text.

And that's basically all they do – predict the next word. When you ask an LLM a question, it doesn't 'understand' in the human sense. Instead, it calculates what response is statistically most likely to be relevant, based on the patterns it's seen during its training. It's like a supercharged version of the autocomplete on your phone, but instead of predicting the next word in a text message, it's generating entire passages of coherent and contextually appropriate language. LLMs are masters of statistical probability in linguistics, the culmination of deep learning applied to language, enabling them to generate text that easily passes the Turing Test, despite having no understanding or consciousness behind their words.

Natural Language Processing

Natural Language Processing (NLP) is a branch of artificial intelligence that focuses on enabling computers to understand and interpret human language in a valuable and meaningful way. Basically, this is what allows an AI model to understand your input, expressed in natural language. It's also used in things like chatbots, translation services, and sentiment analysis – where the model analyses written or spoken content for emotion, tone, or even things like political leaning.

An LLM is a model that can generate text that you might expect to see, NLP is what allows it to respond to you clearly.

Prompt Engineering

This is a very common term, with quite a simple explanation. A 'prompt' is the input you provide a generative AI model, in order to get a response – what you "say" to it.

Prompt engineering is the growing field of developing better and better strategies for how to phrase prompts to get the best quality results. You can think of prompt engineering as the counterpart to natural language processing, coming at it from the other direction. In NLP, computer scientists are working on ways to make machines understand humans. With prompt engineering, we're trying to meet machines halfway, understand how to get our meaning across to them, and structure our requests in a way that they can accurately understand.

Prompt engineering involves not just the phrasing of prompts but also understanding the nuances of how different models interpret these prompts, requiring a blend of linguistic, psychological, and technical insights.

Hallucination

We're not talking fever dreams or suspicious mushrooms here. When AI experiences a hallucination, it means that the model generates information that is incorrect or entirely made up, even though it sounds plausible. This happens because AI isn't a fact-checking machine; it's designed to create responses that fit the prompt based on patterns in its training data. The AI's job is to produce coherent language, not verify the accuracy of the details. So, when it 'hallucinates,' it's doing what it was built to do – generating a response that seems appropriate for the input, even if the facts are wrong. This is why it's crucial to approach AI outputs critically and always verify information, especially when it's presented as factual.

Tokens

With commercially available AI models, you'll often hear people talk about tokens, token limits, and token counts. This refers to how long the prompt and response is. Token counts are a way for AI companies to quantify the amount of work being done using their tools, and charge accordingly.

Functionally though, tokens are far more important. In the case of an LLM, like ChatGPT, the text in your prompt is broken down into pieces, which could be punctuation marks, words, or even just parts of words. So it will take a sentence such as *"Understanding morphemes enhances vocabulary acquisition.*" and convert it into a string of numbers. Here is more or less how the model would break this sentence down:

"Understanding morphemes enhances vocabulary acquisition."

Under | stand | ing | morpheme | s | enhance | s | vocabulary | acquisition | .

The model is only interested in patterns within the language, so the meaning, the conceptual content of those tokens, doesn't actually matter at this point. It might be easier to visualise them as a string of coloured dots instead:

Under | stand | ing | morpheme | s | enhance | s | vocabulary | acquisition | .

● | ● | ● | ● | ● | ● | ● | ● | ● | ●

The model will now look in its training data for something similar. It doesn't need an exact match, it just wants to categorise this string in a grouping that has fairly similar patterns or structure.

For the generative part, the model will look at the type of patterns that typically follow a string of tokens like this, and produce something along those lines. Convert the tokens back into words, and there you are, you've got a coherent text response to some text input.

Key here, again, is that it is focusing only on the patterns of words. Any apparent understanding of the content is simply an emergent appearance, and not really within the model's grasp.[19]

Emergence

Picture a dusk scene. Thin grey clouds streak the sky. Trees and telegraph poles are silhouetted against the waning light. One of the clouds turns abruptly, twisting and weaving across the sky in hypnotic undulating sweeps. Not a cloud, it's a huge flock of starlings, somehow moving as one to put on this beautiful display. This behaviour is called a murmuration, the airborne equivalent to a shoal of fish moving in synchronicity. But how do the

---

[19] This is all a gross oversimplification of course, but is a useful way to approach understanding an LLM's "thought process".

individual birds, or fish, know when to move, and what way the whole shape will flow next?

They don't. Each one is just following a set of simple rules, such as maintaining a certain distance from its neighbours, and the complexity arises as a result. Emergence is the concept of complex and often surprising properties or behaviours arising from simpler base interactions.

Another wonderful example in nature is slime mould, basically goo that spreads out looking for nutrients, looking very much like something out of Stranger Things. Despite lacking a brain or central nervous system, slime mould can sense out food, explore its environment, and reinforce the most efficient pathways. Some species even display a primitive memory, all without a central intelligence running the show.

A great example in physics is wetness. What does it mean for something to be wet? Water is wet, but hard cold ice is not. An individual H_2O molecule could not be described as wet, but get enough of them together, arranged in a particular way, and with the right amount of energy, and the property of wetness emerges.

Emergent abilities in AI models have been a subject of significant research interest. One of the key findings is that as these models scale up in size, they begin to exhibit capabilities that were not present in smaller models. Certain abilities, such as chain-of-thought reasoning allowed larger models to "think logically", for instance performing multi-step arithmetic or solving complex problems by working through a series of intermediate steps before arriving at a final answer.

We said earlier that LLMs lack a conceptual understanding of the information they're expressing. They're just looking at what they've seen so far, checking this against their training data, and spitting out some text that seems like it should fit. So, to a lot of people's minds, they're not creating something new, even if what they write has never been written before. And they don't understand what they're saying, even if it's coherent and increasingly logical. But if it looks like a duck, and quacks like a duck... How long before a truer conceptual understanding of the world emerges from the system?[20]

LLMs already exhibit cross-domain knowledge application, the ability to apply knowledge from one field to another. For example, applying medical knowledge to answer questions about health implications in fitness or nutrition contexts. There is a logical connection between these two areas, but that connection may not necessarily be made in the model's training data. So even though we know that the LLM is not designed for conceptual understanding, in cross-domain know-ledge application and reasoning, we can start to see the seeds of that emergent property.

Of course, emergence has not been observed only in language models. One of the most obvious and easy to understand examples is in models simulating swarm behaviour (e.g., models of bird flocking or fish schooling). We see complex group formations and movements arising, just like in nature. We

---

[20] Those keen to point out that AI is locked inside a machine, and can't really understand because it lacks experience of the real world, would do well to remember that they are essentially just brains, riding around on skeletons.

understand that these behaviours are the result of simple rules followed by each individual agent, so it's no surprise at all really. Just like in nature, the rules that are being followed can be shaped by environmental rewards. In the case of birds and fish, it's survival and procreation. With robot swarms, we can use reinforcement learning to reward success at certain tasks. We need only set the objective and allow the model to create the rules, coming up with simple and effective ways for the machines to organise themselves to complete tasks without central control. The applications are potentially very broad, and though alarmists will often bring up terrifying things like military "kill-swarms",[21] we could also picture things like earthquake-rescue swarms, quickly finding survivors in the rubble.

In other examples, it's harder to pin down what exactly is happening, as totally original approaches are being used, and we're not always sure how the models came up with them. Reinforcement learning models, trained to play games such as chess

---

[21] To be fair, this is very alarming and not at all impossible. The war in Ukraine has already proven the importance of small battlefield drones, and advanced military drone strategy. It's not a big step to take.

and go, have developed strategies and moves that are highly innovative and were previously unknown to human experts.[22]

An oft-cited example is Alpha Go's "Move 37" in its game against Lee Sedol in 2016. Go is a dazzlingly complex board game requiring intuition, creativity and strategic thinking. Alpha Go's ability to beat accomplished human players was considered something of a breakthrough in AI, since Go is considerably more difficult to solve than chess, something AI has been able to trounce human masters at since the late 90s.

What's significant about Move 37 was that it was totally unexpected. At the time, Sedol was the second highest ranked player in the world, but no human player would have made that move. The move itself might not be called an emergent property, but the ability to create such a totally novel strategy was. Alpha Go hadn't combined moves or strategies it had seen before in an interesting way, it had displayed an understanding

---

[22] despite literally thousands of years of study and strategy development.

of the game and come up with something completely different. Sedol was blindsided, although he countered masterfully. Alpha Go eventually won the game, with many commentators noting that some of its moves that initially looked like mistakes eventually revealed hidden strategies.

Emergent properties in AI, particularly in LLMs, are subject to a lot of hype. It's easy to dramatise a "step change", where the model's ability to perform certain tasks suddenly leaps up out of nothing. Two things to remember here:

1. The way in which AI companies quantify these abilities has been shown to be flawed.[23] Essentially, if you count only complete success and ignore the results which are *almost* there, then when the model gets to the 100% mark, its ability score suddenly shoots up. In reality though, there may have been a slow and steady build up.

2. However, this doesn't discount the emergence in itself. It just frames it in a less dramatic way.

---

[23] In a Cornell study in April 2023, Schaeffer et al. re-examined the data using different approaches, and showed a different statistical narrative.

Scientific advancement is usually slow and boring, however exciting we want it to be.

As we watch out for cross-domain knowledge application and novel strategic thinking in AI models, there is the possibility of new discoveries, not just in the results that mathematical models deliver, but in the routes they take to get to those conclusions. If we can understand the methodologies being employed, we may find whole new approaches to doing science, which could unlock entire fields of study.

The continued advancement of these emergent abilities may also bring AI across the step from narrow to general intelligence.

Agents

Agents refer to autonomous entities or systems that can take *actions* to achieve specific goals. In a sense, a robot vacuum cleaner is an AI agent. It perceives its environment through sensors, makes decisions on how to navigate around your apartment. Typically these days however, we're talking about an online tool that can do something in the real world. A virtual personal assistant like Siri or Alexa, for example, can process your voice commands and then perform tasks, such as updating your calendar or order groceries.

When you combine multiple AI agents, each with a specific task or focus, it greatly multiplies the overall capacity of the AI system. This is because each agent brings its own specialised skills and together they can handle more complex, multi-step tasks. Instead of one agent trying to do everything, multiple agents can focus on different areas, making the system more efficient and capable.

This is especially interesting, as you can combine agents with different capabilities or specialties, along with a central agent whose purpose is to coordinate them. For example, imagine an AI tool that has one agent for booking flights, another for comparing hotel prices, and another for scheduling meetings. On their own, these agents can perform their individual tasks well, but when combined, they can work together to plan an entire trip for you. This approach turns what could be many smaller, narrow

AI systems into one larger, more cohesive and capable AI tool.

Narrow AI

Narrow AI is the type of artificial intelligence we have at the moment, focusing on a single function or a set of closely related activities. Its scope is narrow, although the application may be broad. So even though we may be able to use a tool like ChatGPT to do many different things, it's not the tool that achieves the result – it's the way in which we wield it.

Narrow AI operates based on patterns and data it has been trained on, without any real understanding or awareness of the content or context.

Fans of the animated TV series Futurama might recall that Bender was a bending robot. His programming allowed him to bend iron bars, but not straighten them again. For that, you'd need an "un-bender". We can think of Narrow AI, very loosely, like that, although this cartoon character clearly possessed the next level of intelligence, AGI.

AGI (Artificial General Intelligence)

Human-level AI, General AI, or most commonly Artificial General Intelligence (AGI), refers to broadly intelligent, context-aware machines.

A machine with this level of artificial intelligence could *truly* understand[24], learn, and apply its intelligence to solve any problem, much like a human being.

An AGI would be capable of abstract thinking, problem-solving, and decision-making across diverse fields – from composing music to developing scientific theories, from making ethical decisions to inventing new technologies. A key difference here is that just one general AI model would in theory be able to do all of those things, without needing much in the way of human guidance or application as a mere tool. Imagine all the speed of a supercomputer, the breadth of knowledge of the whole internet, and the reasoning and planning ability of a capable human being.

---

[24] As opposed to LLMs just *appearing* to understand

The development of AGI poses significant risks and ethical questions. These include the potential for misuse, the impact on employment, challenges in ensuring ethical decision-making by machines, and the difficulty in controlling or predicting an AGI's actions. Whether AGI would merit legal rights is also a topic of much debate. While it may exhibit behaviours or decision-making processes similar to human intelligence, does this equate to consciousness – with self-awareness and subjective experiences?

Even more so than intelligence, consciousness is firmly in the "we have no idea what it is" category. If and when we get to that point, we will need to consider some very serious ethical questions around machine rights and personhood.

The Singularity

The singularity is the hypothetical future point at which AGI surpasses human intelligence. If we think about the speed at which tech is improving, and particularly taking into account the possibility of AI being employed to[25] develop even more powerful machine intelligences, this threshold could be passed very very quickly after we achieve AGI. It's speculated that the singularity would be utterly transformational, leading to fantastic advances in technology and, some would say inevitably, superintelligence.

Superintelligence

Superintelligence, in its broadest sense, refers to an intellect that significantly surpasses the cognitive abilities of humans in virtually all domains, including creativity, general wisdom, and problem-solving. The implications of such a development are profound, offering both unparalleled opportunities and unprecedented challenges, potentially re-shaping everything from our daily lives to the very essence of humanity.

This has long been the stuff of science fiction, with sometimes benevolent but more often malevolent and frightening depictions – think HAL in 2001: A

---

[25] or deciding to

Space Odyssey or Skynet in the Terminator franchise. Perhaps because of these depictions, and maybe because we find it uncomfortable to think about ourselves as inferior beings, it's easy to dismiss this idea as pure fantasy. Why, though, if artificial intelligence is getting smarter, faster, and more powerful all the time, would it suddenly level off when it's reached our level of intelligence?

Ray Kurzweil, text-to-speech pioneer and prominent futurist, views superintelligence as the next step in evolution, predicting that:

"Artificial intelligence will reach human levels by around 2029. Follow that out further to, say, 2045, we will have multiplied the intelligence, the human biological machine intelligence of our civilisation a billion-fold."

The End of Seeing and Believing

Carbon-14, a radioactive isotope, is naturally present in all living things. It's formed in the upper atmosphere, when cosmic rays from outer space collide with nitrogen atoms, resulting in a nuclear reaction that transforms the nitrogen into an unstable form of carbon. This carbon atom then joins up into carbon dioxide, and is eventually absorbed by a plant and enters the food chain.

Scientists can use this phenomenon as a dating tool because when an organism dies, it stops absorbing carbon-14, and the isotope decays at a known rate. After 5,730 years, half of the carbon-14 will have transformed back into nitrogen. By measuring the ratio carbon-14 to carbon-12 (regular carbon) in an artefact, scientists can estimate its age.

Then, all of a sudden, along came the atomic bomb tests in the 1950s and 1960s, releasing a significant amount of additional carbon-14 into the atmosphere, and putting off its natural levels. This "bomb carbon" skewed the accuracy of carbon-14 dating for objects from the mid-20th century onwards. We could no longer be certain how old something was.

Thankfully, atmospheric atomic bomb testing was banned in 1963, and nuclear detonations are now very rare. Scientists had to recalibrate their measurements to account for the 20th century spike, but we're back to having carbon dating as a relatively reliable tool.

Now, post-2023, another fundamental shift has occurred. Just a few years ago, almost every artificial thing around you involved direct human thinking or decision-making. With the advent of sophisticated artificial intelligence, that's no longer certain. As this new "bomb media" permeates the socio-cultural environment, we can be less and less sure what's man-made, AI-generated, old, new, false, or true.

We're already straining the limits of our ability to distinguish fact from fiction online, and can see this bleeding into broader societal structures such as journalism, legal evidence, and intellectual property.

You may have heard the term "post-truth" used to describe this problem. It first popped up in the 90s, but is becoming a more and more accurate descriptor of the reality we live in. Post-truth refers to a cultural and political context where objective facts are less influential in shaping public opinion than appeals to emotion and personal belief. This phenomenon is not just about the availability of false information; it's about how we react to all information, true or false.

American comedian Jordan Klepper has famously interviewed Trump supporters during and since the 2016 presidential campaign. He often "traps" his subjects by getting them to expose the contradictions in their own logic. In an interview on the Daily Show, he described one of his most poignant moments, interviewing a woman during the first impeachment hearing. Insisting on his innocence, she told Klepper that if Trump was doing something wrong, he'd be trying to hide it.

Klepper asked, "Well if he was stopping people from testifying, then that would be an admission of guilt, right?"

"Of course," she responded, "of course."

When Klepper told her that Trump was indeed blocking John Bolton from testifying, she took a long pause, and then said, "I don't care."

He was taken aback by her complete honesty in that moment, later reflecting that we no longer have politics about *what you want*, rather politics about *who you are*.

> "*We're not really coming to an understanding of truth; that's who that person is and they don't give a shit about [a] new piece of information.*"

This anecdote is the perfect epitome of post-truth thinking. There are two important things I'd like to note here, however:

> Firstly, that this is quite an extreme and overt example. People exhibit post-truth thinking on a smaller scale all the time, and in fact it's those more subtle acts of wilful blindness that may do more harm, since their very subtlety makes them easier to ignore.

And secondly, that yes, this is an example from the right, but there are of course plenty of examples from all across the political spectrum. In fact, a big part of those rationalisations are based on "otherhood" – You disagree with the left, the right, this view, that view; and look – there are crazy irrational people on that side. This reinforces what you already believe to be true, and so you double down on your opinion, and all the post-truth smoothings over seem more justifiable.

Social media often takes the brunt of the blame for this shift in attitudes, and of course it plays a huge part, since it's how we interact online, but one of the major causes, as I see things, is the sheer volume of information that's available to us. We're simply not able to deal with that amount of data, and so in the face of a potentially traumatic overload, we cling to the most comfortable ideas, those that align with our world view. The echo chamber isn't just online, it's in our heads.

The generational shift in media consumption over the past few decades has been dramatic. In my grandmother's time, there was the BBC. It was a trusted source, despite its biases. You may agree or disagree with what they said or how they framed things, but you knew the facts they were presenting would have some substance. This generation often places higher trust in "official" sources of information.

Today's media landscape is a different kettle of fish. Not only do we have a proliferation of "less-official" information sources.[26] Traditional media, still the loudest voice in the content cacophony, is marred by increasingly poor journalism. Copy-and-paste research has compounding effects on even innocently misconstrued or misportrayed information.

The eroded trust in traditional sources has, for some, led to a total rejection of established media. This rejection often manifests not just as scepticism but as contrarianism and outright denial, even in the face of factual evidence, and the rise in popularity of conspiracy groups like QAnon, which spread ideas that can lead otherwise rational people to act in potentially dangerous ways, as they grasp for a sense of control in a system they feel powerless in.

These are serious societal issues that have been building for a long time but really came to the fore over the past

---

[26] And this includes both nonsense spouting loonies at the fringes of the political spectrum and legitimate information from small, niche, or marginalised perspectives that would otherwise go without a voice. The problem is, how can you differentiate?

decade or so. Looking forward, think of the potential that AI-generated content has to make things worse. Any bad actor – or even an incompetent well-meaning actor – now has the ability to create content en masse, which could reinforce existing conspiracy theories or even spawn new ones. The content need not even be super realistic or convincing; it just needs to be everywhere. As expert marketeer Joseph Goebbels knew, if you say something often enough, it becomes fact.

Society will likely adapt and people will develop mechanisms for dealing with these issues. However, as I've mentioned before, such changes take a long time, and the dangerous period of disruption is what's in front of us right now. Adding generative AI to the mix is really throwing petrol on the fire.

And let's widen our scope beyond political concerns. What happens when you can't trust *anything*, not just a news story or "fact" you read online?

In 1991, Jean Baudrillard's essay, "The Gulf War Did Not Take Place," presented a thought-provoking perspective on the nature of reality in the context of media representation. Baudrillard argued that the Gulf War, as presented by the media, was not the actual war but a hyperreal version, a simulation that the public consumed. He wasn't really denying the Gulf War happened; his point was to challenge our understanding of how the media shapes our perception of events.

How can you prove it was true? It all comes down to trust. Either you were there, or you trust a person who was there and can confirm it, or you trust the news reports. Unless you were *actually there*, you don't have first-hand information. Baudrillard's essay was an interesting thought experiment on the power of the media, but in today's era of easily created deepfakes, it starts to resonate in a different way. What happens when a video call from what seems clearly to be a friend or loved one may not be real?

A 'deepfake' is a fake image or recording of a real human being, created using deep learning algorithms. The AI is trained on images, video, or audio of that person, and can accurately mimic their voice, appearance, and even mannerisms.

Imagine a scenario where you receive a call, and the voice on the other end is indistinguishable from your child's, asking you to double check their social security number, or asking if you could wire them money to deal with a minor emergency. This is not a hypothetical future, it's now. Cybersecurity experts have raised alarms about the advancements in deepfake technology, which now allow fraudsters to mimic someone's voice, appearance, and even mannerisms in real time. The technology's growing efficiency means that even a basic gaming computer can now be used for creating deepfakes, making it broadly accessible.

Deepfake technology, once something that required sophisticated expertise, a lot of time and effort, and a huge amount of training data, has evolved. Now, a mere five minutes of audio or a couple of hours of video are sufficient to create a convincing fake. Think of all the pictures and videos of you that are easily accessible on your social media accounts or elsewhere online.

In a 2023 article in the LA Times, Jon Healy described real-time deepfakes being used for corporate espionage, to influence voters, take advantage of lonely men and women in catfishing scams, and to trick people into sending money to "relatives". One 23-year-old man apparently used the "grandchild in distress" trick to swindle $200,000 from elderly people in Newfoundland over just three days.

Defences against deepfakes are emerging but are often playing catch-up. To guard against such sophisticated scams, experts are recommending very simple counter-measures. Families are encouraged to establish a code word or phrase, kept secret within the family and not shared anywhere online. This could act as a failsafe against imposters claiming to be a family member. The effectiveness of this technique is questionable though, considering that one relative we all have, who'll happily share their mother's maiden name, date of birth, and favourite internet password in a quiz to find out which Disney character they are.

Beyond just families and close friend groups, businesses are also vulnerable to real-time deepfakes. Employees may be tricked into believing they are communicating with a colleague or boss, leading to potential security breaches. The secret code-word idea really breaks down when we're talking about even a moderately-sized workforce.

At present, experts advocate for vigilance during video calls. Look for anomalies, such as disproportionate blinking, mismatched facial features, or unrealistic reflections in glasses. More interactive tests, like asking the person on the other end to perform specific physical actions, can also help in identifying deepfakes. As technology advances, however, even these clues might become less reliable.

Societally, we might eventually see the adoption of new heuristics for identifying AI-generated content, so that checks in interpersonal interactions become second nature to us. The contemporary debate around data privacy may mature into a society that is both closed off and connected, with people broadly adhering to an etiquette that may seem cold to us today. A wonderful representation of this is portrayed, subtly, in the 2021 film *After Yang*. This science fiction story focuses on social impacts of technology, and its world is wonderfully informed by contemporary debate around personal privacy issues, spying from tech companies, and what it means to have privacy in a massively connected world. The extrapolated future etiquette around personal privacy was most notable, perhaps, in an interaction between the protagonist and a café manager. He's trying to find a former employee, who he doesn't know directly, but the manager is very cautious about revealing anything.

"You've never met her?

No.

And you don't know her name?

No.

Yeah... Then I don't either. Sorry."

What's striking here is that the interaction is not confrontational. There's an understanding that the protagonist's request is pushing a little on socially accepted norms, and there's no attempt to press the point or convince the manager with excuses, as we might expect in a similar situation set nowadays.

Another possibility, of course, is that society will lapse towards a more confrontational, insular paranoia. Think of times when we believed that faerie folk came out at night to steal away our loved ones, and interactions were underlain with deep-rooted suspicion. There's been a meme knocking around the internet, making just this comparison:

> *"It's funny how recognising AI art nowadays is just the same rules as recognising the fae in old tales.*
>
> *'Count the fingers, count the knuckles,*
> *count the teeth, check the shadows,*
> *If they ask a question, you should always lie,*
> *and never, ever make deals with their kind.' "*

In the corporate world, reliance on voice or facial recognition as sole security measures is increasingly risky. The sophistication of deepfakes means that traditional biometric safeguards are becoming obsolete. This calls for a shift towards more analogue methods of verification, even reverting to in-person meetings, to ascertain the authenticity of interactions.

With digital media's authenticity in question, analogue media like tape recordings, photographic film, and hand-written letters could become more trusted forms of communication, used for sensitive messages. However, the limitation lies in their dissemination. These formats lack the speed and reach of digital media, significantly constraining their effectiveness in today's interconnected world.

Right now, we're all at least a little aware of the possibility of data breaches, identity theft, and so on. But it's quite easy to dismiss on a day-to-day level, since we rarely communicate anything that would be of value to spies or scammers. They'd need to go to an enormous effort to access our data and personal content, before then having to sift through it to find the one or two useful nuggets, which might then only yield a tiny reward. So it's certainly not worth our hassle in suffering delays, particularly on important issues.

In the near future though, this accessing, stealing, and sifting might not be so difficult at all, and could easily be done on a mass scale. With the effort so small, then the risk to reward ratio becomes more and more appealing.

So, all of this centres on security and trust issues spilling out from the digital into the real. What about the valuable content that already resides purely in the digital?

In the realm of content creation, AI is threatening to undermine traditional concepts around intellectual property (IP) and authorship. Historically, IP laws have been built around the idea that creative works are direct products of human intellect – reflecting an individual's creativity, skill, and often a unique style. AI disrupts this notion by introducing a non-human actor that can produce works reminiscent of human creativity but without the same personal investment or creative process. This shift raises fundamental questions: who owns an AI-generated piece of art, and how do we attribute authorship when the 'creator' is a machine learning algorithm trained on a vast array of human-generated content? Who is held accountable for copyright infringement or plagiarism claims; Is it the prompter, the tech company, the AI model itself?

As we confront these challenges, potential technological solutions like blockchain, the technology behind crypto-currency, have been suggested for establishing digital content authenticity. Blockchain's decentralised and tamper-evident ledger could provide a way to verify the originality of digital content. However, we're missing an important point here. The issue isn't that an AI model might directly plagiarise an artist's image, a musician's melody, or an author's text. It's that they can do what that creator does, one thousandfold faster, and one thousandfold more prolifically.

Our current legislation is all based around human's ability to copy other humans. There's an understanding that it's normal, natural, and encourageable to be inspired by someone else's work, but we're not expecting people to be able to so shockingly outperform and overwhelm the originator of a style or movement. Sure, some have more resources at their disposal; industries frequently chew up little creators, crush their dreams, and churn out cheap derivatives on a mass market level; but that's the David vs Goliath worst-case for a creator in our present world.

Pretty soon, *all* human creators could be reduced to Davids, simply unable to compete.

Once more, this is not some theoretical dilemma for the far-flung future. The complexities of AI in relation to IP laws have been brought into sharp focus by a slew of court cases. As I'm writing this, it's early 2024, and already this year, we've seen a series of court decisions and procedural rulings in lawsuits filed over the use of creative content by generative AI programs. Many of these lawsuits allege copyright infringement due to the unlicensed use of copyrighted works by AI companies in training their models.

In class action suits against generative AI tools like ChatGPT, plaintiffs argue that these tools and their outputs are "derivative works" of the creative labour of others. The allegation is that AI tools use extensive amounts of copyrighted material to produce "human-seeming text" and that this large-scale use threatens the livelihoods of creators and infringes on their copyrights.

One notable case is Getty Images vs. Stability AI, which is being tried both in the U.S. and in the High Court in London. This case challenges the use of copyrighted material in training the latest generation of AI by major tech firms including OpenAI, Meta, and Google's parent company Alphabet. Another case involves three illustrators suing Midjourney, also for allegedly using their works to train AI model without their consent.[27] These lawsuits highlight a critical tension point: AI tools are trained on vast datasets, often scraped from the internet, which include copyrighted materials. The plaintiffs argue that this constitutes copyright infringement, as their creative works are essentially being used to train systems that then replicate their style or elements of their work, potentially for profit.

However, the central question is whether the use of copyrighted material to train an AI model constitutes plagiarism or fair use. After all, the process involves transforming the original work to create something new. Again, in our current legal system, we're set up to judge human vs human, and I can't help but see it as fair use if we're going to apply these rulings broadly. Imagine the implications of essentially banning research, inspiration, and media consumption by anyone who might then produce more media.

---

[27] This one is personally relevant to me – my wife was named in the lawsuit as one of a few thousand artists proven to have had images of their works used in training the AI.

AI's ability to generate content that mirrors human creativity tests the limits of current IP frameworks. The very definition of authorship is predicated on human involvement, yet AI operates independently once it is trained. This independence, coupled with the AI's capacity to learn from existing copyrighted works, creates a legal and ethical conundrum. The traditional IP landscape, designed to protect and incentivise human creativity, now faces a scenario where the 'creator' does not inherently possess the attributes (like consciousness or intent) that IP laws were designed to safeguard. What isn't *fair* is pitting us against the machine, but we're likely a very long way from that sort of formal legal acknowledgement.

Another sector that's bristling over AI-generated content is education. We're seeing a plagiarism panic in schools and universities at the moment. Traditionally, plagiarism in academic settings has been a significant concern, with educational institutions implementing stringent measures to detect and deter students from copying text from human-written sources. However, as AI's capability to generate original, coherent, and contextually relevant text grows, the very concept of plagiarism may undergo a fundamental shift. In a world where students have access to AI tools that can produce essays, reports, and research papers, the act of 'ripping text' from existing human-written sources becomes almost obsolete.

This shift challenges the traditional mechanisms of enforcing academic integrity. The ease with which students can now generate content tailored to specific questions or topics using AI tools means that educators and institutions need to rethink their approach to plagiarism. It's not just about detecting copied content anymore; it's about understanding the origin of the work – whether it's the student's own intellect or an AI's output.

Calculators were once seen as a threat to learning basic arithmetic, but are now a standard tool in maths classes. In my day, maths teachers endlessly droned their mantra, "You won't always have a calculator in your pocket." But now it's twenty years later and I do have a calculator in my pocket, all the time. In fact, I have a computer that I can ask basically any question, and it will find whatever information I want. AI is the next logical step, and has the potential to be a powerful tool in academia, aiding in research, idea generation, and even *improving* writing skills.

The key question is: What are we preparing students for? If the goal of education is to equip students for a world increasingly integrated with AI, then banning AI tools is short-sighted lunacy. Instead, the focus should shift towards teaching students how to use AI responsibly and effectively, integrating it into their learning process while maintaining the core values of critical thinking and creativity. Brent Anders, director of the Center for Teaching and Learning at the American University of Armenia, discusses this concept at length in his book, The AI Literacy Imperative. He envisions a future where educators, though still needing subject matter expertise, will focus more on students' developmental path and motivation. Leaning on their interpersonal skills and emotional intelligence, teachers and lecturers would take on more of a guidance and support role.

Anders also posits that human professors in third-level education may not be a given. Many, even most, university courses could be entirely self-studied, with chatbot support.

> *"Having a real teacher ... will be seen as a greater luxury. Less funded universities will have many more courses that [are] completely automated."*

In an environment where AI assistance in academic work is assumed, traditional methods of testing and evaluation no longer fit the bill. We need alternative approaches that put more emphasis on conceptual understanding and critical thinking. The current system of tests and written essays is a product of practicality in a world where we have millions of students going through courses, and we need to prove that they're earning their qualification. We need to validate the efficacy of their education. If we can no longer rely on written submissions – and we can't – then we need to look towards things like oral exams, open-book assessments, and practical applications of knowledge.

By shifting towards project-based learning, we can assess students on their ability to apply knowledge in real-world scenarios, collaborate with others, and think critically. In assignments like this, AI is an invaluable tool, which students should be encouraged to use, in fact taught how to use most effectively, rather than being hobbled.

Incorporating AI into the learning process, where students use tools under guided conditions, can help educators assess how students augment their work with technology, rather than using it as a crutch. Assignments that require unique, creative solutions or in-depth analysis of complex problems can nurture a student's creative thinking, critical thinking, and collaborative skills.

As AI reshapes the academic world, educators and institutions must reimagine traditional practices of teaching, learning, and assessment to prepare students for a future where AI is an integral part of work and life, and to respond to reality. It's here, shift gear, Get used to it!

The knee-jerk reaction of many institutions unfortunately has been an attempt at prohibition. Just like the court cases around IP and copyright, they're trying to shoehorn the issue into existing structures. The problem is that this totally misses the point.

Missing the Point

On the night of April 14, 1912, Captain Edward J. Smith received several iceberg warnings. As the evening progressed, lookouts Frederick Fleet and Reginald Lee began their watch. The night was unusually calm, making it difficult to spot icebergs, as calmer water meant that there would be no white line of waves breaking at their bases. Compounding the difficulty was the absence of binoculars in the crow's nest, which had been misplaced.

At about 11:35 PM, Fleet saw a large berg in the ship's path and sounded the alert by ringing the bell three times. He then made a call to the bridge. Upon receiving the warning, First Officer William Murdoch, who was in charge at the time, ordered the ship to turn "hard a-starboard" (to the left) and reversed the engines. Despite these efforts, at 11:40 PM, the Titanic's starboard side scraped along the iceberg, causing critical damage. She sank beneath the waves a few hours later, taking 1,500 souls with her.

Most everybody reading this, I think it's safe to assume, will have heard of the Titanic, and will be aware that there were a series of mistakes, oversights, and poor decisions which ultimately led to or contributed to that disaster. I'd like to focus on just one, however – William Murdoch's decision to reverse the engines. There is a theory that if he had powered ahead full speed, instead of slowing the ship down, the Titanic would have turned quickly enough to avoid the iceberg's death blow.

Let's skip ahead a few decades to the late 20th century, where another iceberg was looming. A technology emerged that would irreversibly transform the music industry. Compact Discs (CDs) had been introduced at the start of the 80s, but it wasn't until the early 90s that they started to achieve dominance. This change wasn't so disruptive, really. One type of product, the vinyl record, was being replaced by another. In fact, the industry was invigorated. Everyone and their mums were rushing out to buy new, fancy CD players. Of course for listening on the move, audiotape cassettes were still the norm. A CD would skip and jump horribly if the device was shaken, so it was a while before you got reliable players in cars, and even longer before the discman replaced the walkman. It's incredible to think that there are so many people now out there, possibly even reading this book, who are technically, legally, considered fully grown adults, but who have never practised the steady careful gait required to prevent a discman in one's pocket from skipping.

By the mid to late 90s, two other acronyms had become widely familiar, CD-R and CD-RW. Now the content on CDs could be written or even re-written. This meant that instead of spending £25 on a new album, you could borrow your friend's CD and in just half an hour, with a reasonably powerful computer, make your own copy!

Record companies of course began experimenting with various copy protection technologies on audio CDs. Laws were tweaked and adapted, and vendors selling knock-off albums often faced severe punishment, widely publicised to set an example. These measures were met with mixed success however, and there was still a steady stream of music being copied privately.

The MPEG-1 Audio Layer III, or MP3, would turn this stream into a tsunami. This wasn't a new hardware technology like CDs, minidiscs, walkmen, or CD writers; it was a software technology. MP3s compressed music files to about a tenth of their original size without significantly compromising audio quality. This innovation made it feasible to download and share music over the nascent internet, where bandwidth and storage space were precious commodities. Suddenly, entire music libraries could fit on a small USB stick and be swapped and shared in seconds. Importantly, they could be quickly and easily shared online.

A flurry of peer-to-peer file-sharing sites ensued, the most infamous being Napster. Founded in 1999, Napster utilised the MP3 format to enable users worldwide to share and download music completely *for free*. At its peak, Napster boasted over 80 million registered users. Over just two years of activity, it's estimated that several petabytes[28] of data passed through the site, at a time when we were still dealing in MB; it would be another ten years before computers commonly came with 1TB of memory.

The music industry, anchored in traditional distribution models, was completely unprepared for this digital uprising. Major record labels and industry bodies reacted by launching legal battles against Napster and others. These did succeed, in the short term, Napster was shut down in 2001. This defensive stance was aimed to protect established revenue streams, primarily from physical sales,

---

[28] a petabyte is just over a thousand TB

which in 2000 alone accounted for almost $14 billion in the U.S.

In the long-term however, the war on MP3s would never be won. The industry's initial reaction to file-sharing was arguably shortsighted. Their business model was based on people buying CDs: music as a product. In their rush to protect that model, they didn't look at the big picture, to see a total paradigm shift: music as content. Music as content was not just an alternative to music as a product, it totally shattered the concept. It was years before the industry finally accepted the need to change, adapt, and create a new business model that suited their new reality. This resistance to change ultimately cost the industry dearly, as global recorded music revenues plummeted. Over the ensuing decade, sales fell from that $14B figure for physical sales down to just $7B for all sales.

Eventually, the music industry began to adapt. Artists shifted focus to live performances, and record labels set their sights on streaming platforms like Spotify. Greater emphasis has also been placed on licensing for films, advertisements, and video games.

One wonders what losses could have been avoided, and innovations fostered if, instead of reversing engines like

Murdoch on the Titanic, the industry had ordered full speed ahead, and turned hard-a-starboard.

The war on MP3s could be quite instructive for the art world. In the previous chapter we looked at the first battles of the war on AI-generated content. This is a war in which the status quo is also doomed to defeat. I don't see a solution, within the existing paradigm of content creation as protected by IP and copyright, that would prevent artists drowning at the feet of AI.

The inevitability of technological progress necessitates a re-envisioning of the future. Just as the music industry adapted to digital distribution and streaming, the art world may need to explore new models of compensation and recognition for artists. We're not talking about innovative licensing agreements for the use of a creator's style[29] or contributions to AI training datasets; these ideas just expand on what we have now, adding frankly unmanageable forms of acknowledgment that respect the original creators' influence on AI-generated works. What we need is a completely and utterly different approach to how creators are compensated for their work. A more promising seed to build on is Patreon – fans directly

---

[29] Try defining the "style" of millions of artists in clear legal terms.

supporting the creators whose work they enjoy. As the name suggests, Patreon is essentially a crowdfunding site allowing ordinary people to become patrons of the arts, by donating small sums to their chosen creators. I'm not suggesting the democratisation of artistic merit here, that would be dreadful, but think of it as the starting point for an alternative compensation model. I don't create something and then sell it, the value of my creative contribution is recognised, and I am compensated for the time, effort, and relative impact of that contribution.

Again, I'm not suggesting a concrete solution here; I unfortunately don't have the answers. The bigger point is that we need to look at the impact of AI on an industry, and imagine a new system, based on that reality, not to paper over the cracks it causes in the current system.

So how can we avoid falling into the same familiar mental traps, and foster, in ourselves and others, big-picture thinking?

The bad news is that big-picture thinking is a fairly complicated thing to define. There's no easy wave of the magic wand that will make you into a big-picture thinker.

The good news, however, is that there's a whole world of research, advice, and information out there on "How to Train Your Brain". You can find a myriad articles, podcasts, and self-help books; with the usual amount of questionable fluff, but a large chunk of it firmly grounded in the fields of psychology and metacognition. There are some really solid techniques and exercises you can engage in, which will contribute to a gradual shift in your mindset. And it should be a gradual shift we're after here, building solid foundations and growing new approaches in your thought processes.

Metacognition is a good place to start on this journey. It will give us the lay of the land, and allow us to con-textualise the route we're taking.

"Cognition" means thinking – fairly simple – so the important part is "Meta". Meta isn't just the name of Zuckerberg's insidious megacorporation. A prefix from Greek, it means "beyond," "after," or "behind." In contemporary usage, it tends to indicate a concept which is an abstraction from another concept, making it a higher level or self-referential.

For example, in the game of Dungeons and Dragons, players act out scenarios in a fantasy world. They ideally stay in character throughout, maintaining the integrity of the game's immersive role-playing and narrative-driven structure. To do so, they are generally discouraged from "being meta" – speaking too much about game mechanics like die rolls or attack points, as this crosses the line between what the player knows and what their character knows.

Metacognition, so, is the practice of thinking about thinking. More than just introspection, it's about being aware of the game mechanics affecting how we think, learn, and problem-solve.

This is something I often work on with my students. They might have a blocker, something they just can't grasp. Rather than banging their heads against the wall with endless drills and rote repetition, we can take a metacognitive approach, reflecting on their learning process, the structures in their native language that frame the expression of a similar concept, and how those structures are different in the target language. We could also look at their particular learning style, and find an approach that will feel more comfortable and engaging for them, helping them to adapt their study habits and become a more effective learner.

Within metacognition, there are many different "types" of thinking, four of which we could say are fundamental to big-picture thinking:

Critical Thinking

Critical thinking is the ability to think clearly and rationally, understanding the logical connections between ideas. It involves being able to actively and skilfully cut through the noise and evaluate information gathered from observation, experience, reflection, reasoning, or communication. In simpler terms, it's about being able to objectively examine and question ideas and assumptions rather than accepting them at face value. Critical thinkers can identify, construct, and evaluate arguments, and are able to spot inconsistencies or mistakes in reasoning. This kind of thinking leads to well-developed conclusions and solutions, and it values evidence over personal beliefs or biases.

In an age of information overload, saturated with fake-news, critical thinking is a vital ability to ensure our judgments are sound and well-founded. As AI swells the sea of mis- and disinformation by orders of magnitude, this may be the most important skill that we can teach ourselves and our children, so that we become intuitive fact-checkers, difficult to dupe and measuredly sceptical.

Lateral Thinking

Lateral thinking is a problem-solving approach that involves looking at a situation or problem from a new or different perspective. It's about creatively thinking outside the box to find unconventional solutions.

Rather than following a traditional, logical path, lateral thinkers explore various angles and possibilities that might not be immediately obvious. This type of thinking is particularly useful for generating innovative ideas and solutions that traditional, linear thinking might not uncover.

In the tumult of societal disruption, we can no longer fall back on well-worn, trusted routes. As SoftwareONE's Dr. Serena Gonsalves-Fersch put it, when speaking on learning & development approaches for firms wanting to weather the AI storm, "business as usual is delusional & irrelevant". If we're to address the new post-AI reality, lateral thinking is a way of getting out of that rut, clearing away traditional starting points, and finding the best angles of approach.

Systems Thinking

While critical and lateral thinking are important in laying the groundwork, systems thinking is an approach that *really* takes the wider view. It's a way of understanding and solving complex problems by looking at them as parts of an interconnected system.

The focus is on how different parts of a system connect and affect each other, more than on the individual attributes of each part separately. In systems thinking, you consider the relationships, patterns, and dynamics within the system to understand how changes in one area can impact the whole. When employing systems thinking, we're conceptualising a web of processes, entities, and dependencies, almost like it's physically woven from string. If you pull on it at this point, or cut it at that point, how will the rest of the web react? What new pathways emerge?

It's a way to hypothesise on a grand scale, zooming in here to make an adjustment, and then zooming out to see the pattern of cause and effect rippling across the world.

Holistic Thinking

Holistic thinking is another approach where you consider an entire system rather than just its constituent parts. The key difference is that while in systems thinking, you're focusing on the dynamics, structures, and patterns within a system; in holistic thinking you're focusing on completeness. You're looking at things as a whole, taking into account all aspects, including, for example, the physical, emotional, social, and environmental factors.

It's particularly relevant in fields like healthcare, education, and personal development, where understanding the complete picture of a person's life or situation is crucial.

While a systems thinker may see a pattern of golden waves and ripples and try to understand the wind with its complex eddies and vortices, a holistic thinker sees the individual stalks of wheat, each with its own slender stem, its roots and the soil that feeds it, its neighbours sheltering and competing with it, and its the precious kernels of its seed, held up for the wind to move.

By looking at these different thinking styles and approaches, we're ourselves taking a holistic view. They're not just methods of thought; they're different lenses, telescopes through which we can view the world in great detail.

Most everybody has come across the beautiful images of distant galaxies and nebulae captured by astronomers. Some of you might not know that these images are not at all what you would see with the human eye.

By using telescopes equipped with different sensors, astronomers take images at different ranges of wavelengths of light. The images are processed, and assigned a colour that we can actually see, like red for infrared or blue for ultraviolet. Then the images are overlaid and combined, creating a single, comprehensive view, presented in a way that we can understand.

For really insightful big-picture thinking, that's what we need to do. By embracing different modes of thinking, we equip ourselves with a comprehensive set of lenses, each suited for gleaning an understanding from its particular perspective.

As lateral is to critical thinking, holistic thinking is to systems thinking. Critical and systems thinking are very logical and analytical, making it easy for us to hone in and become blinkered. We need this ability, if we're to effectively focus on a process or logical chain and follow it through. Lateral and holistic thinking force us to take a step back, breathe, and slowly absorb all of the information. We're required to defocus, break away from the sharper detail and see the shape of things.

Now that we've laid the groundwork, I'd like to share some practical advice and techniques that you can use to foster big-picture thinking. We can break these down into two key areas, passive and active approaches. You could also think of these as long-term and short-term approaches.

What I'll define as passive approaches to big-picture thinking are those that build habits, nurture traits, and tease out new perspectives.[30] They are your bread and butter, the nourishment that will allow your mind to grow.

Active approaches are exercises and thought experiments that will require a short but dedicated time commitment. They focus on putting the skills into practice and consciously honing your abilities. Anyone who has taken a business studies class will be familiar with SWOT analyses and mind-mapping exercises.

Personally, I'd prefer to skip the active approaches. Others might actually enjoy them, but I always seem to find excuses not to put the time in. If we want to make some brain-training progress, however, both approaches really are essential. It would be like a body-builder drinking a load of protein shakes, but then not going to the gym. No pain, no gain.

---

[30] These could still be activities that take effort, but the impact on your thought processes is passive, secondary.

I'm aware that some people might have it the other way around, so remember that this cuts both ways. Motivation can be hard here because, unlike going to the gym, there are no physical changes to show your work is paying off. The best way to ensure you stick to the path is just to carve out set times in your schedule, and build all of these practices into a routine that works for you.

Passive Approaches

Let's start with the fun stuff. If you want to become a big-picture thinker, you're going to need to broaden your mind. The cornerstone of this is *curiosity*. Interestingly, curiosity has been coming up again and again at education conferences lately, as a key attribute that could give humans an edge over AI. I'm not sure how much I agree with that – now certainly, but it's not beyond belief to imagine an information-hungry machine intelligence being trained to execute that imperative creatively – but I definitely agree that curiosity is a trait we need to embrace and nurture. With all of mankind's knowledge available to us through the internet, and now AI tools to organise and deliver it for us with the minimum of effort, any education system focused on knowledge retention techniques is going to struggle to be relevant. A focus on curiosity, exploration, and discovery, however, would imbue in students a drive to question, make connections, and learn.

So how can we foster that drive in ourselves? If the question sounds silly to you, then skip on ahead a few paragraphs, but bear in mind that a mindset of curiosity doesn't come to everyone equally. That's not to say that the capacity varies greatly – I strongly believe that human beings are innately curious animals – but in real life, curiosity is a luxury. If your mind is full of stress and pressure – kids, work, bills, rent, health, relationships; real problems, basically – it's going to be very difficult to slip in and out of a contemplative mindset. That's why super-rich people are always off finding themselves on expensive meditation retreats.[31]

Unfortunately I don't have the answers to all of life's problems, and can't alleviate your everyday stresses, but If you find it hard to feel motivatedly curious, there is one little trick I could offer: Plant a seed in a pre-existing coping mechanism. We all have little indulgences that get us through the day, give us our fix, and allow some

---

[31] I'm not necessarily knocking this, if you enjoy it and can afford the time and money then good for you. Go for it.

escapism from the grind. There's an opportunity there to transplant other little habits and activities that might fulfil the same purpose, but put our minds on a different footing.

A particularly common habit, one which is ripe for replacement, is the mindless scroll. If you find yourself flicking through TikTok or Instagram stories, or meandering aimlessly through the bowels of Facebook and LinkedIn, take a step back and examine why. This is key, we're not just saying "scrolling is bad, stop it." We don't necessarily want to remove these habits altogether, as they may fulfil a function. So, think about them systematically and holistically. In terms of your day, your routine, and your mental & emotional state,[32] what role or effect does the habit have?

Typically, I'll end up scrolling away for two reasons – either I'm bored and don't know what to do with myself, or I'm overwhelmed with tasks and find myself vapidly procrastinating, instead of tackling any of them.

Case A is easy – it's a straight-up substitution, like swapping cigarettes for gum. If you're scrolling out of boredom, you'll find yourself automatically going through

---

[32] Don't leave out that last one, it's important.

the motions. We don't need to go into detail here about all the ways social media is set up to be addictive and insinuate itself into your every waking moment, I think that's fairly well established at this point. But how do we fix it, what can we effectively substitute it with? Sure, you could just exert the self-control to be mindful and live in the moment, but if it was that easy, everyone would just quit smoking cold-turkey. Luckily, there are a whole host of apps that are designed to give you a similar dopamine hit, but which are more conducive to curious or contemplative mindsets. Try to swap out social media with your favourite language learning app, for example.

For Case B – defensive procrastination in the face of overwhelming workload, – it's a bit harder. We want to replace the mechanism, not just the habit. So let's delve a little deeper into my example. The trigger seems clear enough – I have too many things on my plate, and I can't focus on any of them, so I end up scrolling away, watching "just one more" YouTube short for half an hour and not getting anything done.

Are there any other factors at play? Instead of just thinking "why do I do this?", think "why don't I do something else?".

This can indicate reasons you're retaining the habit, rather than just excuses for falling into it. I don't do my work because I'm overwhelmed, stressed, and can't focus on one task because I start thinking about the other tasks.

So, a little breakthrough there – what I really need is to clear my mind and regain my focus. Much easier said than done, but maybe I should have a total break, and room to breathe.

Why don't I just do that – take a proper break, get away from the computer?

Well, I feel pressure to get the work done, so I can't just leave my desk. Hence my ending up at my desk, not getting the work done.

But therein lies the key. If I'm not getting the work done at my desk, then there's no difference if I do something else altogether. I might spend, on average, 15 minutes procrastinating, so, as soon as I find myself starting, I could take a real break, stretch my legs, and clear my head. Different things will work for different people; some may physically go for a walk around the block, others may just grab a coffee and sit looking out the window for a bit. The important thing is to find a substitute that's consistently going to take up that 15 minutes, put you in the right mindset, and also provide your vital dopamine hit. Dopamine is the reward chemical in your brain, which gives you feelings of pleasure, satisfaction and motivation. It's been shown that social media interactions can trigger dopamine release, which makes scrolling more addictive. When weaning yourself away from a dopamine-inducing activity, it's vital to incorporate a small aspect of pleasure. This could be as simple as eating a square of chocolate, listening to music, or interacting with a pet. Once you've decided on your replacement activity, make a new habit of it. Every time you find yourself procrastination scrolling, off you go.

Now some might point out that in that second example, we didn't necessarily insert a habit that fosters curiosity. However, holistically thinking, the knock-on effect of defensive procrastination is a feeling of tiredness, boredom, and disengagement. By cutting that out, and fostering habits that settle and relax your mind, you're better setting yourself up for the rest of the day.

It's important to clear the way, as well as tread the path.

So, curiosity is one important factor. But there's more to it than just that. Let's try to visualise the key elements you'll need in fostering big-picture thinking:

Imagine yourself sitting on a chair in a small room. You could touch the walls and ceiling without leaving your seat. The room is our space for information, wisdom, ideas. We want to make it as big as possible.

Curiosity allows you to expand your breadth of interest. When we add that, we can push out the walls to either side of you. You can now picture yourself facing the wall, but in a long corridor, with new topics filling up the space to your left and right.

To push out the walls in front and behind you, you'll need to increase your depth of knowledge. **Continuous Learning** empowers you to chase details and reasons. You can now picture the room as a vast space, expanding all around you.

But the ceiling is still low, giving a heavy, oppressive feeling. As we've discussed, it can feel impossible to grow if all of your stresses and problems are weighing on you. By getting yourself into the right mindset, allowing yourself to relax, you can push up the ceiling, and literally give yourself some **Headspace**.

This is the feeling we're aiming for, a vast open room, filled with knowledge to consume and ideas to pursue. Curiosity, Headspace, and Continuous Learning will all get you there.

But we're missing the most important element. You're still sitting in your chair, looking around you. You can only see one side of the picture. To look at things from every angle, you'll need to get up out of your comfort zone and walk around. **Diverse Perspectives** are the final element, and by embracing that, you can really start to understand the world, and think big.

Now we know where our sights are set, let's look at some simple habits and activities that can start to get us there. Remember that these are still passive approaches. Their immediate impact is small and may even seem insignificant but, taken together over time, they're a surefire way to get your brain in gear.

Mindfulness

Mindfulness often carries misconceptions that can put people off before they really understand what it is. Many associate it with hippie culture or new age spirituality, leading us to believe that it's more about esoteric practices than practical mental health strategies.

In reality, mindfulness is fairly straightforward. When we talk about being fully present and "in the moment", we're describing the act of cutting out the buzz in our heads, and not thinking about anything beyond what's in front of us right now. It's a lot easier said than done, halting that inner monologue.

Typically, it's easiest to start with a simple action to focus on. This could be as simple as paying close attention to your breathing, the sensation of walking, or the experience of eating something. The goal is to cultivate a greater awareness and clarity of mind. With a bit of practice, you can calm yourself into a mindful state on demand and engage in fairly objective metacognition, allowing yourself to feel feelings and observe your own thought patterns, almost from a secondary, outside perspective.

Blindboy Boatclub, a prominent Irish author and philosopher, provides insightful perspectives on mindfulness in his podcast. He often discusses mental health and touts mindful meditation practices as an excellent way to ground yourself against stress and other negative emotions. He notes that children naturally exhibit mindfulness, showing immense curiosity about their surroundings. As adults, we often lose this sense of wonder, but mindfulness helps us regain it. According to Blindboy, the only time many adults engage in mindful observation is when on holiday, captivated by new environments and allowing themselves to enjoy them. This shift in focus reveals mindfulness as a state where one is fully immersed in the beauty and uniqueness of the present.

Blindboy used the act of eating an orange to vividly describe the process of focusing on a simple action to exercise mindful thinking.

He suggests experiencing the orange with all senses:

observing its colour and texture, listening to the sound it makes when peeled, and savouring its scent and taste. This exercise is not just about enjoying the fruit but about practising focus. By directing your full attention to the orange, you momentarily free yourself from all other concerns. Eventually, when you've developed the ability to enter that state of mind easily, you'll be able to do away with the orange and just take a step away from yourself whenever you need to get some perspective.

Achieving a calm and controlled dissociative state can declutter the mind, making room for clearer, more focused thought. It sharpens you by stripping away superfluous thoughts and stresses, improving your capacity for thoughtful introspection and dynamic problem-solving.

Idle Hands, Idle Mind

While mindfulness can help us get away from the whirlwind in our heads, there are also times when you want to do just the opposite. Rather than controlling and focusing your thoughts, you can let them do their thing and play themselves out. Particularly with bursts of creativity, one of the easiest ways to stifle and overwork your ideas is to start working on them before you're ready – before they've had the chance to crystallise in your head.

Most people will have, at some point, experienced that manic enthusiasm that comes when we get really excited about something. A great way to handle this is to engage in some physical activity that you can do on autopilot, something that doesn't require your full attention. This can be as simple as doing the dishes or going for a walk. Often, I find that working with my hands – making, organising, or fixing something – can allow me to engage just the surface-level, practical part of my mind and let my subconscious fire away in the background. Rather than chasing conclusions, let the ideas come to you.

One of the big problems with modern life is that we don't allow ourselves the space to *think* anymore. We're constantly active consumers of media. The upside to this is that we now have the ability to absorb information and nuance much more quickly than previous generations. Think of jokes in the 1990s. When I was a kid, a joke was a long story where everything had to be explained, the situation set, characters introduced, and it would then end in a punchline, something that gives the narrative a sense of completion and creates humour based on the context you've had to set up with the story. Nowadays, a joke is more often just an image with perhaps a couple of words of text. Our ability to understand internet memes so instantly is actually very interesting. The humour here is totally contextual and often grounded in an abstraction of the zeitgeist, very self-referential and metacognitive.

We hear every so often that social media is destroying the English language, our attention spans, or our ability to interact with each other. While there are arguments to be made, this isn't really the case. What's happening is that the way in which we absorb social information and process language and ideas is simply evolving into something different. While our use of language does seem at times to be simplifying, the nuance formerly coded in the specificity of our words is now coded in visual fluency. With a shorter attention span comes faster uptake.

However, one thing we do seem to be struggling with is the space to stop, think, and process the information we've absorbed. Because we're taking in so much all the time, we aren't actually dwelling on very much of it, and this is a very important process – not just in retaining knowledge, but in creating a deeper understanding and fundamentally building our own opinions about things, making connections between that which hasn't been spelled out for us. The ability to parse nuanced social irony in the subtext of an image should make us all superstars in connecting the dots. But unless we have the time to connect the less immediate dots, we're wasting this ability.

So, back to physical tasks that free the mind: remember always the purpose for engaging in these passive exercises. We want to slowly build habits and shape mental pathways that will foster that wider, big-picture perspective. The way that you approach your own mindset is like a tool. If applied correctly, you can exact the result you want. So, the next time you are brimming with ideas or just really fascinated by something and find yourself thinking about it over and over – whether it's academic, professional, or personal – find something to do with your hands or your body, particularly something that's going to take a chunk of time.

You might surprise yourself with the conclusions and epiphanies that pop into your head, and at the very least, you'll get the ironing done.

Valuable Media Consumption

Many of us find ourselves immersed (trapped) in a constant stream of media consumption these days. The type of media you consume can significantly influence your thought processes. It's not just about the information it provides; it's also about how it challenges your perspectives, encourages deeper thinking, and *sparks your interest*. Valuable media should be something that sticks in your head, and you find yourself thinking about it throughout the day. It should give you that tickle of curiosity, wanting to learn more. It might also give you the urge to share what you've learned and discuss the ideas with someone else.

Ideally, you watch, read, or listen to something and then find yourself running it over in your head while doing the dishes, recommending it to a friend the next day, and throwing a dash of what you took from it into conversations during the week. At this point, you should take two steps:

1. Explore the seam.

    You've found a great source, see what else it has to offer. Is there more from the same creator, with the same presenter, or from the same company?

2. Pull at the thread.

    Your interest is now piqued. Capitalise on that! Go forth and google; find out more on the topic or the ideas that got you so interested. Make sure to use critical thinking to fact check, examine the information you were presented with, and dig up sources.

Let's look at some different types of valuable media consumption[33] and how you might integrate them into your routine:

Podcasts: Listening to podcasts on diverse topics can expose you to new ideas and viewpoints. There's a whole world of podcasts out there, on topics from science and history to culture and philosophy. But don't feel like it needs to be academic. As long as you get that spark of interest, you're still learning. If you don't enjoy it, you won't pay attention anyway.

Also think about *why* you enjoy it. Look out for podcasts you enjoy because of the information, story, perspectives, or opinions they offer.

Avoid podcasts about something you're already familiar with. The aim is to challenge yourself and broaden your knowledge.

The best time and place for podcasts is when you're doing something else. This is long-form content, so you'll need 30 minutes at least. Listen as you drive to work, walk to the shops, or do the housework.

---

[33] This might seem super rudimentary, but it's how you go about it that counts. How do you make time, and how do you approach the task?

Perhaps you have some paperwork or manual work that doesn't require your fullest attention. Try to make it a habit, so always listen to podcasts during these activities. If you enjoy the show, that's great. If you don't - why not? Critique is a worthwhile mental exercise.

Music: Music is like food or air; it nourishes the soul. It's also something that fires us up or fills us with nostalgia. In this case, however, we shouldn't look at the music you know and love already. Exploring new music, from different genres, times, or places around the world can offer insights into different cultures and histories. There are stories behind every song and every artist.

You might start with something familiar, and work from there. Think of a band, artist, or song that you love and look into its roots. Who were the influences? What genres are they drawing from or rejecting? Examine the homage, pastiche, and pushback, and go digging there.

Another approach is to spin a globe, pick a random place on the map, and find out about the music from there. It could be traditional, classical, or popular, as long as it's new to you.

Once you find something you like, don't just add it to your Spotify playlist and have it in rotation. Pull at the thread, find out more about it – the story, the fashion, the culture. Music has an amazing way of making us feel connected to places and ideas, so having that background information, that context, will bring it to the fore whenever you hear it. *Now* you can add it to your playlist.

Reading: I remember being shocked as a teenager to learn that many of my peers did not read. Not that they could not read, but that a significant minority of them did not read for pleasure, and many avoided all text outside that which was compulsory for school. Perhaps it was my naivety, more likely my then unacknowledged privilege, but it was an earth-shaking discovery.

I have always been a bibliophile, and habitually tore through books at a ferocious rate. Part of the privilege I mention is that this was actively and deliberately instilled in me by my parents, from a very early age. Another is my not having dyslexia, something that in my school days was just about becoming widely accepted and understood.

All of this could have led me towards an opinion that unfortunately still abounds, among readers and non-readers alike, that quantity matters, and there is value in amassing a great pile of finished books, proving your intellect. However, this could not be further from the truth. There are two main fonts of value in reading, particularly for our purposes. One is the absorption of concepts, narratives, and perspectives – easily achieved through other media, such as audiobooks, if that's your preference. The other is the state induced by the act itself. This requires immersive reading, without struggle. As you read the words written by another, you parse them in your own voice, inferring your own tone and inflection from the pace of the text. This ability is almost magical, quite possibly the closest thing we have to telepathy; you are absorbing the thoughts and ideas of another person, directly inside your head. This magic does not require quantity to be effective, although it may be something that many of us need to work at.

The concept of a "finished" book is something else I'd like to touch on. For some reason, it's accepted that we can enjoy music and films over and over, but re-reading the same book can be looked down upon. If you have something that puts you into that absorptive mindset and sparks your intrigue, then think of it like a favourite album. I've been re-reading the same thirty-odd books as my staple for the past decade[34], and continue to pull new things from them each time.

The final myth to dispel here is that you should focus on great literature, heavy academic tomes, or the broadly lauded award-winners. Bringing this section back on topic, we are looking for habit-forming activities that will over time foster big-picture thinking. Reading books and articles across various genres and fields, including fiction and non-fiction, narrative and factual, verbose grandiosity or plain and simple, all broadens your perspective.

---

[34] Though not exclusively, of course.

For just absorbing the information, as I mentioned, audiobooks are a fantastic resource, but remember that we also want to foster the meditative, receptive state that comes with immersive reading. If that doesn't come naturally to you, you may need to actively work on it. Start small, and be disciplined. Carve out a small time each day, at least twenty minutes, and above all else – find something you enjoy reading.

Video: Taken together, video may constitute the largest category of media that we regularly consume. Between TV, movies, long-form, and short-form online videos, a significant portion of our time is spent glued to the screen. Studies put the average between five and ten hours per day.

Almost all of what I've said on other media forms can apply here – don't feel like you need to stick to academic or intellectual content, focus on things that spark interest and provoke thought, and consider different sources for diverse perspectives.

There is a trap to beware of falling into though, particularly with short-form online video content. The line between a four or five-minute informative video and a thirty-second instant-gratification hit is a very thin one. The problem isn't that interesting information can't be conveyed in such short clips – it can – but that for most people, it quickly becomes a comfortable way to pacify the mind, which is the opposite of what we're after. Of course, some of you might be able to effectively consume media in this way and feel invigorated and engaged, but I'd wager that it's an extremely rare ability. Remember to question yourself metacognitively; what am I getting out of this, how does it make me feel, and make me think?

That may be the key to all of the passive approaches to fostering big-picture thinking. Engage in metacognition, holistically analysing the impact of habits and stimuli, and exert some control over the road they lead you down. The mind is a malleable thing, and it's up to you what shape you want it to take.

This mind-shaping will instil or expand on the abilities you need, but to effectively put those abilities into practice, you'll need to actively hone your skills.

Active Approaches

While passive approaches to big-picture thinking are indirect and gradual, active approaches are more deliberate and immediate. They require setting aside time and mental space to engage in exercises specifically designed to stretch and develop our capacity for big-picture thinking. This section explores various structured exercises and their application, and reflects on how these exercises can help to develop different thinking apparatuses.

The Five Whys: A Drill Down to Root Causes

The 1920s in Japan were a period of rapid industrialisation. Sakichi Toyoda, a self-made inventor with a shock of white hair and an insatiable curiosity, was laying the groundwork for what would become a global giant – Toyota.

Since the 1890s Sakichi had been designing and building looms. His company, Toyoda Automatic Loom Works, was a bustling hive of whirring machinery and industrious workers. Sakichi wasn't just interested in *building* looms; he was obsessed with making them better. He believed in "Jidoka,"[35] a philosophy that empowered workers to identify and solve problems on the assembly line. This meant fostering a culture of questioning and continuous improvement.

Imagine a young weaver noticing a broken thread on her loom. In a typical factory, she might simply signal for a replacement and keep working. But Sakichi envisioned something different. He wanted her to ask "why" the thread broke. Was it a faulty material? A misaligned setting? By delving deeper, the weaver wouldn't just solve the immediate problem; she'd prevent it from happening again.

This seed of questioning blossomed in the 1930s as Sakichi's son, Kiichiro Toyoda, took the reins of the company. The world was in the throes of the Great Depression, and Japan's fledgling auto industry was

---

[35] Also known as autonomation – "automation with a human touch"

no exception. Unlike their American counterparts, Toyota couldn't afford massive production lines or overflowing warehouses of parts. They needed to be efficient, resourceful, and above all, good at solving problems. When a problem arose, be it a faulty engine part or a production bottleneck, workers wouldn't just slap on a band aid solution. They'd relentlessly ask "why", peeling back the layers to expose the root cause.

The Five Whys became a cornerstone of Toyota's approach to mass production, helping to propel them to the forefront of the global auto industry. This deceptively simple technique, likely honed from Sakichi's emphasis on Jidoka, is a structured approach to uncovering the roots of a problem, not just the immediate or surface-level symptom. It's a simple yet powerful technique that strengthens critical thinking in several ways:

- **Causal Analysis:**

   It encourages you to think systematically about cause-and-effect relationships, identifying the chain of events leading to a problem.

- **Identifying Assumptions:**

  It challenges you to examine your initial assumptions about the problem and dig deeper for underlying reasons.

- **Questioning Everything:**

  It fosters a questioning mindset, prompting you not just to stop at the first "why".

By practising the Five Whys, you develop the critical thinking skills necessary to analyse situations objectively, identify root causes, and make informed decisions for long-term solutions.

How it Works:

Define the Problem: Start by clearly stating the problem you're trying to solve. Be as specific as possible.

Ask "Why?" the First Time: Identify the first cause that seems to be directly responsible for the problem.

Repeat "Why?" Four More Times:[36] The root cause is typically the last answer in the chain of "whys" that is beyond your control or requires a fundamental change to address.

For Example:

- **Problem:** The machine malfunctioned and stopped production.

- **Why?** The pressure gauge malfunctioned.

- **Why?** A faulty sensor provided inaccurate pressure readings.

- **Why?** The sensor wasn't properly calibrated during the last maintenance cycle.

- **Why?** The maintenance technician was overloaded with tasks and missed this critical step.

- **Why?** We don't have enough technicians to ensure proper maintenance procedures are followed.

---

[36] The number five is something that appears to have been formalised gradually, but should be taken with a pinch of salt. As with all such techniques, it's important to bear the point in mind. Finding the root cause may actually take three or ten "whys".

This example is a very clean and simple one. In cases with more complexity, it's important to realise that the Five Whys won't always lead you to *the* root cause, but it will certainly help to identify *a* key root factor.

Let's take a more complex social problem:

- **Problem:** High schools are seeing high dropout rates.

- **Why?** Because students feel disengaged from the curriculum.

- **Why?** Because the content often does not seem relevant to their personal lives or future career interests.

- **Why?** Because educational policies and curricula are frequently designed without substantial input from students or consideration of regional and demographic differences.

- **Why?** Because educational systems often prioritise standardised testing and uniform benchmarks over personal learning experiences.

- **Why?** Because these systems are structured to measure and compare academic performance quantitatively across broad populations, often for funding and policy-making decisions.

In this case, five whys definitely led us to a causal factor, which requires a fundamental change, but it's also clear that this isn't the sole factor, and if we took another route of questioning, we may end up with a different answer.

To visualise multiple potential causes at once, we'd need a different exercise, which would help us flex our systems thinking.

Fishbone Diagrams: Unveiling the Skeleton of an Issue

Imagine a fish skeleton, its bones branching out from the spine. Now, picture that spine as the central problem you're facing, and each branch representing a potential contributing factor. This is the essence of a fishbone diagram, also known as an

Ishikawa diagram after its inventor, Kaoru Ishikawa, a Japanese quality management guru.

We're back in mid-20th century Japan, and to another person with a sharp mind and a focus on efficiency. Ishikawa, a quality control engineer in the bustling shipyards of Kawasaki, was determined not to just blame workers for faulty products. He believed the root causes of quality issues lay deeper, within the complex systems of production themselves. He envisioned a way to untangle this web of factors, to see the problem not as a single knot, but as a network of interconnected threads.

Inspiration struck while brainstorming with colleagues. Imagine a fish skeleton, Ishikawa thought, its bones branching out from the spine. He envisioned the central problem as the "fish head," and each branch representing a potential contributing factor. It wasn't just a fancy chart; it was a philosophy – a way of approaching problems not in isolation, but as part of a larger system. Ishikawa's diagram wasn't a magic bullet, but it was a powerful tool for fostering a culture of continuous improvement.

The exercise of creating fishbone diagrams forces you to think about the interconnectedness of a problem. By taking a wider view, and considering interactions and factors, it helps you to foster systems thinking in a number of ways:

- **Identifying Interrelationships:**

  The diagram reveals how different factors can interact and influence each other. For instance, poor machine maintenance (materials) might lead to production delays (methods), which could demotivate workers (people).

- **Uncovering Hidden Factors:**

  By considering various categories, you can discover underlying causes you might have missed otherwise.

- **Promoting Root Cause Analysis:**

  It helps you move beyond superficial symptoms and identify the deeper roots of the problem.

How it Works:

The diagram on its own looks like a fish. We need to fill in the details, starting from the head.

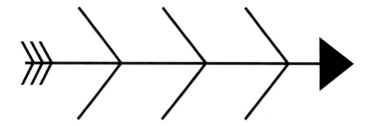

The Head (Problem): This is the central issue you're trying to understand or resolve. Try to define it simply and succinctly.

The Spine (Main Categories): These are the broad categories that might contribute to the problem. Common categories include the five Ms in manufacturing (Manpower, Machine, Material, Method, & Measurement), the eight Ps in marketing (Product, Price, Place, Promotion, People, Process, Proof, & Performance), and the five Ss in service industries (Surroundings, Suppliers, Systems, Skill, Safety)

In order to be effective tools within an organisation, it's often necessary to rely on things like alliteration to make lists easier to remember. When applying this exercise yourself though, don't worry too much about things being neat and clean. Here are key considerations for defining these categories:

- Relevance: Ensure that each category directly relates to the problem being analysed and can logically include potential causes.

- Comprehensiveness: Categories should collectively cover all possible areas where causes may originate, ensuring no potential cause is overlooked.

- Mutual Exclusivity: Each category should be distinct, with minimal overlap between them, to avoid confusion and ensure clarity in where specific causes should be placed.

- Manageability: While categories should be comprehensive, they also need to be manageable. Too many categories can make the diagram overly complex and difficult to use, while too few may oversimplify things.

- Industry or Process Specific: Tailor the categories to fit the specific area or process being examined.

The Bones (Causes): Under each main category, you list specific factors that could be causing the problem. For example, under "people," you might list factors like lack of training or low morale.

At this stage, we're aiming for specificity and inclusivity. Include all possible causes that could contribute to the problem, even if they seem unlikely, and specify them clearly. This ensures a thorough analysis.

In terms of organisation, prioritise causes supported by data or observable evidence and try to move from general to specific as you move outward along the bone. This helps in understanding the relationship between primary and secondary causes. In larger diagrams, you can even include offshoots from the "ribs" so we end up with a feather-like structure.

As an example, let's not look at an industry or business problem, but a social phenomenon. Japan seemed to stand out in my research for these brain training games, and that struck me as interesting. To explore this, I used the question: "Why is the

Japanese approach to efficiency so holistic and well-balanced?"

This led me to identify six key areas that could contribute to this phenomenon, from which I extrapolated sub-points, the ribs for each section, with a bit of help of course from my friendly neighbourhood LLM. This exercise turned out to be quite interesting and sent me down a rabbit hole, learning about Kaizen and Keiretsu, concepts previously unfamiliar to me.

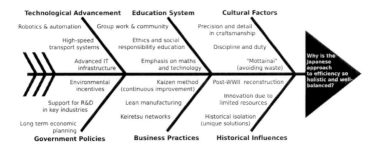

However, it's important to note here – I am in no way an expert on Japanese culture or business practices. So this diagram, resulting from a twenty minute brainstorming session, cannot be taken as definitive fact. But is it still a useful exercise? Yes!

What we are actually doing here is applying the fishbone diagram technique to help visualise the different factors contributing to an idea or concept I'm interested in. This diagram is a structured starting point. When your curiosity is piqued, you should always dig a little deeper, but doing so blindly runs the risk of hopping from rabbit hole to rabbit hole. With a structured approach like this, I can bring some order and coherence to my research and focus on things most relevant to the topic at hand. I may even decide that my initial assumptions were incorrect and might go back and update the diagram again. That's exactly the point of these exercises and why setting aside time for them is so valuable.

Thinking about *diverse perspectives*, if I wanted to pull on this thread a little more, it would be arrogant beyond belief not to go looking for the opinion of an actual Japanese person. It's easy to be curious about something different, other, and foreign, but be careful not to put too much weight on your own assumptions. Get up out of that chair, move around, and preferably identify stakeholders who can guide you and better inform your perspective.

Stakeholder Mapping: Considering Affected Parties

The concept of stakeholder mapping as part of strategic management likely evolved from the broader field of systems thinking and organisational theory, which gained prominence in the mid-20th century. The specific term "stakeholder" was popularised in the 1980s by American R. Edward Freeman, in his landmark book "Strategic Management: A Stakeholder Approach."

Freeman's work emphasised that truly effective management involves paying careful attention to all stakeholders – not just shareholders, suggesting that organisations should map out and understand the interests of all who affect or are affected by the company's operations. This approach helped expand the focus of business strategy to include a wider array of influences and considerations, enhancing holistic thinking in business practices.

The stakeholder mapping exercise offers several benefits for fostering holistic thinking:

- **Broadens Perspectives:**

  It encourages consideration of various viewpoints, ensuring decisions account for diverse impacts and needs.

- **Interconnectivity Awareness:**

  It helps visualise and understand how different parties are interconnected and how actions affect the entire system.

- **Fosters Empathy & Communication:**

  By considering the perspectives of all stakeholders, it nurtures empathy and enhances communication with different groups.

How it Works:

Stakeholder mapping begins by defining a central issue or goal. The process involves identifying all parties (stakeholders) impacted by or capable of impacting the issue. This includes direct actors, secondary influencers, and even peripheral entities. The map looks like a series of concentric circles, which helps you to visualise the degrees of separation for each type of stakeholder.

Identify the Core Issue: Place the central issue or organisation at the centre of the diagram.

List Primary Stakeholders: Surround the core with a circle of primary stakeholders – those directly impacted by or directly influencing the issue. A good way to separate these groups visually is to keep those who influence the issue at the top, and those who are impacted by it below. Both might apply to some stakeholders, so they can be placed closer to the left or right side of the circle.

Identify Secondary Stakeholders: In the second circle, include those who influence or are impacted indirectly.

Add Tertiary Stakeholders: Include a third circle for stakeholders with less direct connections to the issue but still relevant. You could continue to add periphery circles, but in most cases, this just complicates things. It's best to just keep the third circle quite large, so you can fit everyone in.

Assess Influence or Impact: Now we need to assess the strength of the connection. Think about the power, influence, and interest of each stakeholder. We can visualise this with an arrow. The size of the arrow shows the magnitude of the connection, and the direction shows whether this stakeholder is impacting or impacted by the issue.

Consider Inter-stakeholder Dynamics: We can also consider connections and groupings between stakeholders, by circling them together or adding coloured connecting lines. It's at this point that the diagram tends to get very untidy, so if it's something you want to refer to later, best to take a picture beforehand.

For our purposes though, the *making* of the diagram is what will help to foster holistic thinking, and whole pictures are most often quite messy in real life! There's something about the physicality of drawing circles and lines to connect different parts that gives you an almost visceral understanding of their interconnectedness.

As an example, we could take the acquisition of a local bookshop by a chain franchise. As this is a private acquisition, there are fairly few stakeholders who can exert influence, but as it's an important shop in the community, there are a whole web of tertiary and periphery stakeholders who may be impacted.

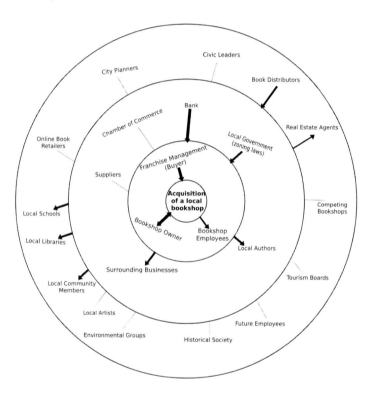

This method trains you to think holistically by requiring you to consider a wide array of influences and outcomes, beyond just the transactional participants. It fosters a deeper understanding of interdependencies and encourages a broader evaluation of potential impacts.

The three exercises I've described so far are all mid-20th century techniques designed for business development. For the fourth exercise, focused on stretching your lateral thinking muscles, I would like to suggest something a little bit different.[37]

WikiWhack

WikiWhack, or Wikipedia Racing, is a game with its origins in the fledgling Internet 2.0 era at the start of the 21st century.

Some among you may remember googlewhacks, which referred to search terms on Google that returned only one result. Now, with the advent of sponsored listings, better search algorithms, and of course, pages listing googlewhack-producing search terms, it's pretty much impossible to find a googlewhack anymore. Obsessions with weird curiosities like this were common in the early days of the internet.

---

[37] If you'd prefer something similar for lateral thinking, I'd recommend SCAMPER, Random Input, or Alternative Uses

This feeling of curiosity and community is what led to the birth of Wikipedia itself. People were enthralled with the connectivity and scale of the information available, and there was great excitement about discovering weird, tiny corners of the web, as if you could explore its physical fringes.

In its simplest form, WikiWhack is a game where players must navigate from one wikipedia page to another in as few clicks as possible. It's typically intended as a two- or multiplayer game, but it's perfectly possible to play on your own, albeit a lot less fun. Wiki Racing can help to sharpen lateral thinking in several significant ways:

- **Connecting Disparate Concepts:**
  It promotes the ability to quickly connect and make associations, facilitating a deeper under-standing of how seemingly unrelated ideas intersect.

- **On-The-Fly Strategising:**
  It Encourages the formulation of strategic pathways under constraints, honing decision-making skills in complex scenarios.

- **Stimulates Creativity:**

  By navigating through unexpected and unfamiliar topics, it fosters a creative thinking process that helps identify novel connections and solutions.

How it Works:

Choose a target and starting point:

Wikipedia's main menu, found on the left side of the screen, has a "Random article" option. Click this twice to find your starting point and target article.

Go!: Navigate from your starting article using Wikipedia's internal links, moving from topic to topic until you reach your target article.

Of course, without many structures and constraints, we can't get the full benefit from this game, and it also quickly devolves into meta-thinking, where players use the structures of Wikipedia itself rather than focusing on the connections between the different topics they're racing through. Because of this, there are a range of variants and optional restrictions that you might choose to employ, both to make the game more challenging and to keep it fresh and fun.

Variations:

- **Clicks to Jesus / Clicks to Hitler:** Often considered the original version of the game, players start from a random article and try to reach Adolf Hitler's page in the fewest clicks. Whether Clicks-to-Jesus emerged as a more acceptable toned-down alternative, or just out of humour is anyone's guess.

- **Time Trials:** Here, the winner is determined by who reaches the designated end page the quickest, rather than by the number of clicks. This is best performed on two computers, starting simultaneously to the roar of a crowd of frantic onlookers.

- **Wiki Grand Tour:** With a list of multiple target articles, players navigate through a predetermined list of articles in sequence, aiming to be the first to complete the tour.

Optional Restrictions:

The general purpose of these rules or restrictions is to prevent shortcuts and promote deeper engagement with the content. A rule of thumb is to disallow anything that makes the game too easy. Examples include:

- You can't use the browser's "Back" button or "Find". Navigation is only by internal links.

- You have to avoid larger pages like "United States," which contain too many links.

- Links in dates, list pages, and discography or bibliography tables are banned.

- If a player hits a dead end (a page without useful links), they're allowed a single use of category links at the bottom of the page to escape, but only once per game.

All of these games and exercises have their intended applications, but we can broaden that scope to suit our own ends. The power in techniques like this lies in the structure. As any artist will tell you, structure and boundaries are actually conducive to creative work and creative thinking because they force you to move forwards in an organised way, thus getting the ball rolling. It provides you with a starting point and a clear direction forward.

Remember to think metacognitively when approaching these exercises. The structure you choose will set you in a particular direction and get you thinking in a particular way. However, structure is not out of your control. Think about how adaptations to the rules or the order in which you approach things might impact the outcome. By approaching this curiously and purposefully, you might spark something new, and you'll also keep the wider goal in mind – improving your ability to think big.

And now that you feel your mind can process concepts and ideas in a broader way, what do you feed into it?

You Are What You Eat

Nobody should be eating dolphin meat. Beyond the ethical and moral considerations, there's a hidden danger lurking within: concentrated levels of highly toxic mercury. This isn't an evolved defence mechanism of marine mammals. Rather, it's the result of a process called bioaccumulation – where certain substances, like mercury, build up in an organism faster than they can be broken down or expelled.

It all starts with us. Human activities such as mining and burning coal for electricity release mercury into the environment. This mercury travels through the air, eventually settling into oceans and waterways far from its original source.

In its initial form, mercury isn't highly toxic.[38] But once it

---

[38] This sounded wrong to me at first but, typically, the mercury released from these processes is elemental, oxidised, or particulate-bound mercury. While these are certainly dangerous, in that initial elemental state they're not as readily absorbed or as toxic as methylmercury.

enters the ocean, it undergoes a sinister transformation. Oceanic bacteria convert inorganic mercury into methylmercury, a toxic compound readily absorbed by living organisms. This methylmercury becomes part of the marine food web, starting with the tiniest of organisms – phytoplankton.

Phytoplankton absorb methylmercury from the water. When small fish or zooplankton consume phytoplankton, they ingest the mercury stored within them. Here's where bioaccumulation kicks into high gear. Each small creature is eaten by a larger one, and at each step up the food chain, predators consume prey that contains small amounts of mercury. Because they eat a lot of prey, the total amount of mercury they ingest and retain grows. This process is known as biomagnification.

By the time we reach top predators like dolphins, swordfish, and sharks, the levels of methylmercury can be millions of times higher than in the surrounding water. The compounding effect of biomagnification means that these majestic creatures carry mercury concentrations harmful to their own health and potentially lethal to humans who consume them.

So, what does this have to do with artificial intelligence?

Just as toxins like mercury accumulate and magnify up the marine food chain, biases can accumulate and amplify within AI systems, leading to skewed or unfair outcomes. It's the technological echo of "you are what you eat." If the training data fed into an AI model is biased, the decisions made by the AI are likely to reflect, or even exacerbate, these biases.

Consider an AI system trained to assess job applications. Humans tend to bring certain preconceptions to the table when screening applicants – about race, gender, socio-economic background, and so on. They're also great at picking up on subtle cues to those points, so it can be quite difficult to get around. It's increasingly common to use an automated system, which is a lot fairer since it's filtering based solely on experience, qualifications, and other predetermined criteria. However, you tend to run into a pigeon-holing problem, where too much focus is placed on box-ticking, and some great applicants get overlooked. Using an AI system seems like a clear step up from this because it could look at each job application as a whole and make a decision based on this broader information. The AI, however, does not actually understand the broader context; it's just a pattern recognition machine. So, we would need to train it on data from human-screened applications, which, of course, is tainted by the biases we mentioned earlier. Not only are we now working with a system that could expound and magnify these inherent biases, but we are also labouring under the false assumption that the issue of human bias has been removed, making it less likely to be addressed in future.

The challenge, then, is ensuring that AI systems are trained on data that's as clean and unbiased as possible. The goal isn't to find perfectly clean data, which is often impossible, it's to understand and correct for these biases during the AI development process. But that's very difficult to achieve when, first of all, most people are not experts in data collection and bias mitigation techniques, and secondly, when you're trying to create something like a facial recognition model, your primary focus will be on getting the model to work. Diversity and inclusion tend to be secondary considerations.

A study by Joy Buolamwini from MIT's Media Lab and Microsoft's Timnit Gebru looked into this in 2018. They discovered that facial recognition systems developed by major companies like Microsoft, IBM, and Megvii performed significantly worse when identifying darker-skinned faces, especially those of women. These AI systems, trained predominantly on datasets filled with lighter-skinned faces, exhibited error rates as low as 1% for light-skinned men but soared to almost 35% for dark-skinned women.

Remember, the model doesn't learn concepts like we do; it learns to pick out patterns you've shown it before. You're not teaching it what faces are, you're telling it to "identify things that look like these". So you end up with a Spot The White Guy machine, which will identify a black woman because she looks more similar to a white male face than a plant pot, not because she clearly has a human face.

Even when assessing the performance of such models, our complacency can be compounded further. Although researchers had claimed an overall accuracy rate of more than 97%, the data set used to assess that performance was itself more than 77% male and more than 83% white.

Again, this issue wasn't necessarily the result of deliberate exclusion or overt racial prejudice by the developers. The environments in which these technologies were developed were often lacking in diversity. Predominantly white and male engineering teams, created datasets that reflected their immediate surroundings. The easiest and most accessible sources of facial images may have been those of themselves, their friends and colleagues, or could have been from publicly available datasets, which also tend to be mostly white. Speak to anyone who's worked a lot with stock photos. It takes a conscious effort to get a good balance of representation and diversity. The developers working on these projects wouldn't have been thinking about those issues as a primary concern – they were focusing on making the technology work. Systemic and subconscious discrimination simply biomagnified its way up the metaphorical food chain.

As we stand on the cusp of building a new world with AI, it's imperative that we remain acutely aware of the prejudices, biases, and systemic issues that shape our current reality. This awareness isn't about placing blame but about taking responsibility.

It's also worth noting that bias, in this context, doesn't always entail social discrimination. Measurements of weather or delivery times could be tainted or skewed, and so paint a slightly inaccurate picture. These types of subtle biases in data could seem quite innocuous but the knock-on effects of badly curated datasets can result in ineffective tools, inaccurate public opinion, and choices that negatively impact us in ways we might not consider, especially if we become over-complacent by putting too much trust in AI-automated decision making. In critical applications like medical diagnosis or criminal justice, the stakes couldn't be higher.

So how do we navigate this?

Data preparation is the process of transforming raw data into a format that AI models can digest and learn from. This is actually where the bulk of the work lies, a meticulous process that ensures the AI doesn't "eat" anything that could lead to undesirable outcomes.

This stage, often referred to as data wrangling or cleaning, is widely regarded as the most time-consuming aspect of developing AI models. It involves gathering, organising, and refining raw data to ensure it's ready for use in training machine learning algorithms. In an LLM, for example, words need to be converted into tokens, and the system for assigning those values, deciding how words or word fragments should be converted into numbers, is fundamental to the success of the model. You can't just pour all the text into a bowl and give it a whisk.

A commonly cited figure is that 70-80% of the work in AI projects is dedicated to data preparation. This estimate has been echoed in industry reports and practitioner surveys over the years. The reality is that AI development is less about glamorous algorithmic innovation than it is months of fiddling with spreadsheets.

The process involves several key steps, beginning with collection. Data is gathered from various sources, such as online databases, sensors, or historical records. Once collected, it undergoes cleaning to address any errors, incomplete information, or irrelevant entries that could confuse the model.

Next is transformation, where the data is standardised into a usable format, often involving converting text into numerical values or normalising categories. This standardisation is key for the AI to be able to compare data collected from different sources, but it can be one of the most challenging phases. Think of all the instances of engineering projects being waylaid over tiny discrepancies. A classic example was NASA's Mars Climate Orbiter mission in 1999. One engineering team used metric units (newton-seconds) while another used imperial units (pound-seconds) for calculating force. This unit mismatch caused the spacecraft to enter Mars' atmosphere at the wrong angle, ultimately destroying it. The disaster was a direct result of a failure to standardise measurements.

In some cases, large datasets need to be reduced in size while maintaining their essential information, to improve processing efficiency. This could mean removing certain sections, which are not relevant to the patterns you're training for, or aggregating granular data points into broader categories. For example, if you have millions of daily transaction records, aggregating them into monthly totals might still give you the insight you need without having to handle the immense volume of raw transactions.

Finally, the data is split into training and validation sets. The AI model is trained, unsurprisingly, on the training data, and the validation data is used to test the model's performance afterwards.

Cleaning, Transforming, Reduction, and Splitting are all quite technical processes, firmly the realm of AI researchers and developers. The collection of data, however, is something we're more likely to have some involvement in, and this is where bias and other errors are most likely to sneak in.

First let's look at a simple question:

What Is Data?

Simply put, data is little bits of information – raw facts and figures that can be collected, measured, analysed, and used to make decisions. Data comes in various forms, from the numbers in a spreadsheet to the words spoken in an interview. In isolation, it's not always meaningful – it's when data is processed, analysed, and interpreted that it transforms into valuable information or insights. It's the foundation upon which we build knowledge, make predictions, and, now, train AI systems.

But not all data is created equal. Some things can be measured directly, whereas others must be interpreted or inferred. In the real world, both types help paint a fuller picture.

For a couple of years, I had the fascinating experience of managing one of Ireland's foremost market research facilities, on Grafton Street in Dublin. It was a place where the mundane met the profound, where everyday preferences became the subject of intense scrutiny.

Picture the scene: In one room, a group of ordinary people from all walks of life – albeit carefully selected and well-defined walks of life – sat around a table discussing their favourite types of jam or how a particular internet service provider made them feel. An expert interviewer guided the conversation, probing deeply into their thoughts and emotional responses.

Behind a mirrored glass wall, a team of corporate executives and sociologists observed intently. Their mission? To interpret these discussions and extract insights that could influence product development, marketing strategies, or even corporate policies.

A lot of effort went into recruiting the respondents and setting up the sessions themselves, often multiple sessions for each project. However, it was after all this that the real magic happened: interpreting the data. Market researchers pored over transcripts and recordings, noted subtle cues, and drew conclusions that numbers alone could never reveal.

This is qualitative research (think "quality"). Because of the effort involved, we could only interview a small number of people. Another approach is to formulate a survey with some really quick and simple questions, and poll as large a number of respondents as possible. This is quantitative research (think "quantity").

Quantitative data can be measured and expressed numerically. It usually comes down to how much, how many, how often, how strongly do you agree. It's straightforward, structured, and easily analysed using statistical methods.

Qualitative data is about understanding the why and how behind the numbers. It requires interpretation, as it's rich in context, emotion, and nuance.

Neural networks and other machine learning models operate on simple numerical representations. To process qualitative or unstructured data, such as natural language, audio, or images, AI models first convert it into numerical values through techniques like tokenisation or pixel mapping. So we lose something of the flavour of qualitative data since it needs to be broken down and expressed quantitatively. We're actually able to infer most of the qualitative essence back, but the more abstract the original information is, the less accurately it can be retained.

So how do companies like OpenAI go about sourcing these huge troves of information? The collection process is often shrouded in secrecy, because these companies tend to operate as private entities with proprietary methods.

Initially, LLM development relied heavily on free, publicly available data scraped from websites using bots, commonly known as web crawlers or spiders, that systematically browse the whole internet and pull out all the text. There are already platforms like Common Crawl, which provide a significant portion of this raw data, offering the text from billions of web pages.

Some freely available datasets and licensed content were used to amass training material. Public repositories like Wikipedia, Project Gutenberg, and various academic databases offer a wealth of information. AI companies' respect for copyright and data privacy though was dubious at best.

Unsurprisingly, this practice is now encountering restrictions. Many websites, including major news organisations, are blocking these crawlers due to concerns about the unethical and uncompensated use of their content. A recent report from the Data Provenance Initiative highlights that between 2023 and 2024, approximately 25% of high-quality data sources were restricted to web crawlers, impacting the ability of companies like OpenAI and Meta to access critical data.

High-profile cases, such as the 2023 lawsuit filed by The New York Times against OpenAI, accuse AI developers of reproducing paywalled content without permission. Similar disputes like Perplexity AI's alleged reproduction of Forbes articles without proper attribution highlight the ongoing tension between AI companies and content providers.

It makes sense that people are less willing to allow their data to be used for free, especially as AI companies profit from it. And as content providers and private individuals alike become more aware of and sensitive to their data being used for training sets, an interesting crisis emerges: the scarcity of data, particularly that which is most high-quality and up-to-date, such as news articles. As a consequence, AI companies may soon run short on fresh, usable data. ChatGPT has almost "finished the internet",[39] in essence, and that spells a lot of difficulty for maintaining its current pace of iteration and improvement.

So, is that the end? Have we reached the peak of AI performance already?

---

[39] Hyperbole, obviously, the internet is huge and always growing. However, diminishing returns from training on redundant or lower-quality data is a big challenge.

Well, there are a couple of factors to consider here. The most important one is that **ChatGPT is not the be-all and end-all of AI.** This is a very common misconception that people run aground on, because of its prominence in the media and because it's likely one of the only AI tools they have consciously interacted with. But, of course, there are many more types of AI than large language models, and all of them require feeding with good-quality data. Given the scale of the companies involved, I'm sure that LLM providers will be able to find ways around the current challenges, even if life moving forward won't be the open buffet it has been for them so far.

So it's increasingly difficult to scrape data from real world sources, but since generative AI can create new content, be it text, audio, images, or video; don't we essentially have an unlimited source of new training data? This is an emerging strategy, known as synthetic data, but it's rife with problems, such as the compounding effect it has on biases within the data. You're not actually introducing new patterns. If anything, you're diluting the level of "real" data in the set.

Even more concerning, since the models themselves are now being used to create a lot of the content that is published online, they're inadvertently gobbling up more and more synthetic data, whether they set out to or not.

A 2023 study conducted by researchers at the University of Tokyo, titled "Will Large-scale Generative Models Corrupt Future Datasets?", looked into this in image generation. In part of the study, real images of elephants were compared with those generated by an AI model. The AI-generated images of course exhibited some strange deformities – extra trunks, too many or too few legs, animals that would never survive in the wild – but perhaps most striking was the aesthetic homogeneity of these images. Many of us are familiar with the particular look common to AI-generated images – over saturation, deep contrast, and unnaturally smooth or sharp lighting.

This uniformity is hypothesised to result from the model's training data being gradually infiltrated by images that were themselves AI-generated. This same effect could easily impact LLMs, video and audio models – anything trained from online content. As AI-generated content proliferates, it becomes part of the dataset that future models train on, reinforcing certain patterns and aesthetics while diminishing diversity and originality. Over time, all of our elephants start to look the same.

We've talked a lot about tools available to the general public, but plenty of AI models are being trained on scientific data, helping us to complete research and even make brand new discoveries.

"We're in luck here," you may be thinking, "scientists' whole job is to collect data carefully and share their results with the world." Like most things, however, it's not really that simple. Although scientific research tends to adhere to much more rigorous standards, they don't tend to adhere to a common format. Scientific papers are not known for their accessible readability. It's a common – and not totally unjustified – trope that scientists tend to be highly intelligent but a little mad and lacking in social skills. Unfortunately for us, they also tend to be lacking in graphic design skills.

Charts, tables, and diagrams vary widely in format and are, for the most part, intended for a readership with an assumed level of expertise in the subject matter. Because of the expertise required in a variety of different fields, the standardisation process for such data can be really difficult. Of course, that's not to say that it can't be done; There are plenty of AI models in use and development at the moment for various scientific subjects, and we're already seeing some unbelievable breakthroughs and advancements because of them. However, as you try to create a larger, broader, and theoretically more generalised scientific model, the formatting discrepancies start to become more and more of an obstacle.

There's another issue we risk running into here, which is that scientific papers and studies are very much fallible and prone to bias, both intentional and unintentional. While it's important to put our trust in science and the scientific method, a cornerstone of this is being open to re-evaluation and scrutiny. This goes particularly for cases where the hypotheses stray ever further from the raw data.

Data is essentially made up of many little facts, points of information that can be simply and objectively expressed. Truth, on the other hand, is interpretive. It's the information you pull from data. Even though we tend to think of true or false as a set binary, everyone, conceptually speaking, has their own subjective truth. And the further you interpret and extrapolate from the data, the more opportunity there is to inject speculation, subjectivity, and bias. Even well-intentioned efforts can falter without rigorous methodology, and it pays never to accept something as fact simply because it's presented so.

Published in 2005, *Freakonomics* quickly became a cultural phenomenon, captivating readers with its unconventional application of economic principles to a wide array of everyday topics. Steven Levitt, an esteemed economist, and Stephen Dubner, a seasoned journalist, teamed up to explore the hidden side of everything – from cheating in sumo wrestling to the socioeconomic patterns of baby names.

The book's allure lies in its creative, lateral-thinking approach. It challenges readers to question conventional wisdom and see the world through a new lens. As someone who read and thoroughly enjoyed Freakonomics, I was fascinated by its ability to make complex economic concepts accessible and engaging. The authors weave intriguing narratives that link seemingly unrelated phenomena, sparking curiosity and encouraging a deeper exploration of societal norms.

The problem with such satisfying and exciting narratives though, is that they are so convincing, especially when delivered with authority and confidence. This point is explored in the podcast *If Books Could Kill*, hosted by journalist Michael Hobbes and lawyer Peter Shamshiri. The show critiques popular books that have significantly influenced public opinion, revealing how they often rest on dubious research and flawed analyses. Through their dissections, the hosts highlight the crucial role of critical thinking and the dangers of accepting data-driven narratives at face value. Their takedown of Freakonomics thoroughly ruined the book for me. Honestly, I felt very disappointed, perhaps even grieving minutely for the high regard I had previously held it in.[40] Fortunately, Hobbes and Shamshiri's irreverent tone and meticulous, almost obsessive, approach to fact-checking is right up my street, so I was mollified by this new distraction.

I do thoroughly recommend the podcast. Although some people may find the tone grating, or even be put off by the strong liberal viewpoint, their critiques are well-researched and there are some wonderful lessons to learn about how misconceptions, fallacies, and pseudoscience can be easily spread. In the case of Freakonomics, there are a few key red flags they point to.

The first is setting up a cult of personality around the author. There's an attempt to present Levitt as both a respected authority and a maverick bad-boy in his field.

---

[40] Take heed of that point. Letting go of ideas and beliefs, even the insignificant ones, even in the face of well laid-out evidence, evokes an emotional pushback.

The trope of the charismatic genius, who's able to make intuitive connections that others miss, is dangerously appealing to us. So much so that we tend to overlook the clear warning signs. In Dubner's original New York Times article on Levitt, which ultimately led to their collaboration on the book, the journalist lauds the economist's creative approach, even when it demonstrably fails:

> *"That paper was later disputed – another graduate student found a serious mathematical mistake in it – but Levitt's ingenuity was obvious."*

Rather than discrediting Levitt's leaping to assumptions, the article goes on to paint him as possessing swaggering common sense, "the guy who sees all the engineers futzing with a broken machine – and then realises that no one has thought to plug it in."

This brings us to another red flag raised in Hobbes and Shamshiri's critique, taking data as a jumping off point, from which to leap to conclusions. Levitt often relies on arguments that appeal to the reader's emotional responses, rather than solid logic. For instance, in comparing the amount spent on US political campaigns to the amount Americans spend on chewing gum, the author gives us a false feeling of things being put into perspective. As Hobbes puts it though, "...those things have nothing to do with each other. You're just juxtaposing an important thing with a frivolous thing to make them both seem frivolous."

The podcast hosts both mention that the parts of the book dealing with descriptive statistics, exposing social trends and interesting correlations, are well written and interesting. However, once the authors start to extrapolate out to specific social insights, they lose their grounding in fact. Again, there's a dangerous appeal in a satisfying narrative. It can lead us to accept hypotheses based on shaky evidence. The whole basis of the Freakonomics approach is using lateral thinking to offer solutions to quite complex social problems. This means that your "smoking gun" is often tangential, so en route to your conclusions, you should be supporting with a lot of corroborating evidence. Because Levitt doesn't do this, the integrity of his claims has to come into question. It turns out that it *has* in fact come into question, and frequently.

I'm sure that given any topic you could imagine, there will be a podcast out there throwing shade and disagreeing. In this case, however, we are supplied with a plethora of sources and references, and a rudimentary online search reveals plenty of critiques from other experts in economics and statistics. While of course there have been cases of establishment blackballers, lashing out at a disruptive newcomer, we should recognise that these are the rare exceptions. Scientific research is rooted in collaboration and corroboration. Where there are a host of experts criticising someone's findings, it's worth taking a look at those criticisms. Do their counter-arguments hold water, or are they too following a particular agenda?

In the podcast, Hobbes and Shamshiri point out a strong conservative bias in Freakonomics, with notable methodological inconsistencies when drawing conclusions in different scenarios. It almost seems like a purposeful agenda on Dubner and Levitt's part:

"[another] way that this book misuses data is leaping to conclusions on some things while refusing to reach conclusions on others."

While the conservative bias is fairly apparent, it's likely not purposeful. The blind leaps of logic and untethering of conclusions from the data leave the door wide open for personal bias and unfounded opinions to taint the outcomes. This is precisely *why* researchers use strict, controlled parameters as much as possible.

One agenda that is almost certainly being pushed deliberately is the sensationalism and digestibility of the narratives being put forth. There is of course a strong motivation for the authors to present dramatic and graspable nuggets of information, so that the book will be more successful and sell more copies.

The oversimplifications that result seriously impact the integrity of their findings, especially when trying to extrapolate from very pared back information. Leaning on just one or two data points makes for easy reading, but breaks down once you apply it to more complex systems. As prominent statisticians Andrew Gelman and Kaiser Fung put it in their 2012 American Scientist article:

> *"What seem like natural calculations are stymied by the impracticality, in real life, of changing one variable while leaving all other variables constant."*

Or as Hobbes puts it:

> *"The whole problem ... is this overconfidence in quantitative data that is completely stripped of all of its societal context. "*

Numbers don't lie, but they are all telling a different story. The challenge for us (as for any reliable AI model we build) is to pull the truth from the cacophony.

As someone who initially found Freakonomics enlightening, the If Books Could Kill episode prompted a stern re-examination of the book's assertions, The engaging storytelling and creative connections that once seemed innovative now appeared, in many instances, to gloss over methodological rigour. This realisation doesn't diminish the value of thinking differently but highlights the importance of grounding such explorations in solid evidence and comprehensive analysis. Hobbes and Shamshiri's critique emphasised several key lessons:

Rigorous Methodology Matters:

Sound conclusions require robust data analysis that accounts for multiple variables and potential confounding factors.

Beware of Oversimplification:

Complex social phenomena rarely have simple explanations. Overly simplistic narratives can obscure the true nature of issues and lead to misguided solutions.

Context Is Crucial:

Understanding the broader context – historical, cultural, socioeconomic – is essential when interpreting data and drawing conclusions.

Question the Narrative:

Engaging critically with popular narratives, especially those that challenge conventional wisdom, helps prevent the uncritical acceptance of flawed reasoning.

But why is all of this relevant? Why does it matter to me?

Well, data is already a massive part of our lives, although mostly hidden in the algorithms we're coming into contact with indirectly through social media and a whole plethora of other automated systems we might not even be aware of. As AI tools, trained on all sorts of data, become more prevalent – especially if that contact remains indirect and, in a sense, hidden from our daily lives – we should make an effort to get to grips with its mechanics and underlying concepts.

A lot of people, from academics like Brent Anders, to industry leaders like Timnit Gebru and Andrew Ng, are advocating for AI literacy, but more fundamental, perhaps, is basic data literacy. I'll go out on a limb here and predict that things will move very quickly indeed, but we're still in the preparatory phase. That is to say, this phase – this narrow window – can be preparatory if we act prudently. The changes that are coming might catch us unawares if we don't start acting soon.

Why should we take any action at all? Surely it's the job of the AI giants to do all this work. As these models become more ubiquitous and therefore more impactful on society, we all have a vested interest in ensuring their efficacy and accuracy. Although I'm not one for offering up my own contributions to the oligarchy, I still want their tools to work well. At the end of the day, it's the digital equivalent of not using plastic straws.

Another, more comfortably self-serving motivation is that by becoming more data literate and engaging with these systems, we can position ourselves to benefit from the opportunities they present. Understanding how AI and data-driven tools work can give us an edge in navigating and even influencing the future landscape, whether in our careers or personal lives. As we've touched on above, AI companies are running into more and more difficulty in sourcing high-quality data. It's not unreasonable to assume that well-tended data sets may garner a healthy payout in years to come, especially in niche, underserved areas that could have critical practical impact.

Leaving aside the idea of training up new tools and models for a moment, there's a huge AI-powered benefit to having your own reliable datasets. AI-driven analytics platforms are revolutionising how researchers and businesses interpret and act on data. These tools use Natural Language Processing (NLP) to allow users to interact with complex datasets simply by asking questions in everyday language. This technology eliminates the need for specialised data science knowledge, making data-driven decision-making more accessible to everyone.[41] Leading platforms like Microsoft Power BI, Tableau, and Zoho Analytics have integrated such AI features already. Although they primarily focus on quantitative analysis at present, the increasing sophistication of NLP means that they are beginning to provide more nuanced insights and recommendations, edging closer to handling qualitative queries and transforming business operations across industries.

---

[41] At the cost, I'm sure, of quite a few analysts' jobs.

Businesses that get themselves into gear early and start gathering, cleaning, and standardising their data will have a significant competitive advantage in a few years' time. Note there were *three* action points there: it's not enough just to collect data – you have to go some way towards cleaning and converting it into a usable format. My competitor might have ten times more data than I, but if mine is better quality, then that's all the advantage I need.

A good place to start if you want to better understand data is to better understand bias. By recognising different types of bias and how we might unwittingly succumb to them, you'll be in a stronger position to critically evaluate data and the conclusions drawn from it.

We can think of our quantitative training data as the phytoplankton at the bottom of our food chain, the foundational element upon which everything else is built. So if our data is flawed – be it biased, inaccurate, or unrepresentative – those flaws can become biomagnified up the food chain as the data feeds into algorithms, models, and ultimately, the decisions that AI makes.

Let's start with another simple question:

What is bias?

Bias can be simply defined as a tendency or inclination to favour one person, group, or thing over another in a way that is often considered unfair or unbalanced. In data and AI, bias refers to systematic errors or patterns in data or models that lead to skewed results.

Not all "bad"or "dirty" data contains bias. *Noisy* data refers to data that contains a high level of random errors or irrelevant information. This "noise" can obscure the underlying patterns and signals, but since it tends to be pretty random, the patterns are still in there, just harder to find.[42] AI models have proven surprisingly efficient at picking out patterns buried under the noise, much better than human analysts. Unlike random noise, bias introduces consistent distortions throughout the dataset, moving everything in one particular direction, patterns and all.

It's incredibly difficult, even impossible, to eliminate totally, especially since it can be introduced into a dataset in so many ways, and at so many different stages.

---

[42] An oversimplification, but more or less true.

Understanding how it works psychologically can help us get to grips with when to expect it. Let's look more closely at a few common types of bias:

Selection Bias

Selection bias occurs when the data collected isn't representative of the population intended to be analysed. As the name suggests, the problem occurs when the data sources are *selected*. For example, conducting a survey about smartphone usage but only polling people in a tech-savvy urban area excludes perspectives from less technologically inclined populations.

In one of the most famous examples, the Literary Digest conducted a poll predicting that Republican candidate Alf Landon would win the 1936 U.S. Presidential election in a landslide over Franklin D. Roosevelt. The poll sampled a massive ten million people, around 8% of the country's population. To reach this many people, they used names collected from telephone directories, automobile registration lists, and club membership rosters. However, telephones and automobiles were still considered luxuries at the time. These lists were therefore mostly composed of wealthier Americans, and weren't representative of the wider population. In reality, Roosevelt won in a landslide.

This type of bias can also occur without an "intentional" act of selection taking place. I recall a memorable, albeit disappointing, dining experience in Lisbon a few years back. My wife and I settled on a highly-rated Mexican place, which had hundreds of five-star reviews. It was quite difficult to reconcile those high expectations with the bowl of rancid guacamole set in front of us, fizzing gently.

It was only later that we realised the restaurant was popular with late-night revellers – drunk tourists and stag parties seeking cheap, greasy food after a night out. The majority of reviews came from patrons who visited while, shall we say, in high spirits. For them, the restaurant hit the spot perfectly.[43] As sober diners seeking a quality meal, our expectations didn't align with the experiences of those reviewers.

---

[43] Tequila.

This is a classic, albeit roundabout, case of selection bias. The reviews we relied upon didn't represent the broader population of diners but rather a specific group with different expectations and circumstances. Because the data sources (the reviewers) were skewed toward a particular segment, our interpretation of the restaurant's quality was misleading.

Response Bias

When collecting data, it's crucial to bear practical and social realities in mind. It's not just a matter of "Who was asked?", but "How were they asked?", and also "Who agreed to answer?". The willingness to respond to surveys can vary widely among different groups, potentially skewing the data. For instance, individuals with strong opinions or those who feel passionately about a topic are more likely to participate, while others may decline.

Additionally, the very act of being surveyed can influence responses. People might tailor their answers to align with what they believe is socially acceptable or what they think the surveyor wants to hear. This phenomenon can also be known as The Hawthorne Effect.

In the 1920s, researchers at the Hawthorne Works electric plant in Illinois were studying how lighting levels affected worker productivity. They found that productivity increased when lighting levels were raised, but surprisingly, it also increased when lighting was lowered. The researchers eventually realised that it wasn't the lighting causing the productivity changes, but rather the workers' awareness that they were being observed. This introduced a form of observer bias, as the workers' behaviour changed simply because they knew they were part of a study.

Confirmation Bias

Confirmation bias is the tendency to search for, interpret, and recall information in a way that confirms one's preexisting beliefs or hypotheses. If information aligns what we already think or know, it's more appealing to us. People tend to be more comfortable with something that reinforces existing thought patterns than something that requires a mental confrontation to resolve.

The controversy surrounding MSG – monosodium glutamate – in Chinese food is a prime example of confirmation bias in action. In 1968, a letter published in the New England Journal of Medicine described a set of symptoms experienced after eating at Chinese restaurants, coining the term "Chinese Restaurant Syndrome." This led to widespread belief that MSG, a common ingredient in Chinese cuisine, caused various symptoms like headaches, dizziness, and chest pain. I remember my parents worrying over this as a child; it would have factored largely in whether we'd eat at certain restaurants.

Despite subsequent research showing that MSG is totally safe for consumption, the public remained convinced of its dangers. Once people believed that MSG was harmful, they began attributing any negative experience related to Chinese food – be it a headache, indigestion, or a bad meal – to MSG. They selectively remembered instances that confirmed their belief while ignoring the countless times they consumed MSG without issue in other foods like processed snacks, soups, or cheese.

Confirmation bias can perpetuate misconceptions even in the face of contradictory evidence. This refusal, or perhaps inability, to change your beliefs based on the reality you're presented with often stems from cognitive dissonance.

Cognitive dissonance is the uncomfortable feeling people get when they hold two conflicting beliefs, ideas, or values, or when their actions contradict their beliefs. To reduce this discomfort, people often try to rationalise or justify their behaviour or beliefs, even if it means ignoring facts or evidence. In this case, it would be uncomfortable to admit having been wrong about something for so long, with so many decisions having been based on it.

In our post-truth society, where subjective feelings and personal beliefs increasingly take precedence over objective facts, this type of cognitive dissonance is becoming more common. People are more likely to hold onto emotionally charged, preconceived beliefs, even when confronted with clear evidence to the contrary. This is compounded further by the fact that simplified information is easier to digest, whereas accurate information sources tend to mention caveats and exceptions, which seem to weaken the point being made, when in fact they should strengthen our confidence in the data collection behind it.

What's particularly concerning is that those willing to change their minds based on facts and evidence appear to be part of a small and shrinking minority.

The Dunning-Kruger Effect

The Dunning-Kruger effect is a cognitive bias where individuals with low ability or knowledge in a particular area wildly overestimate their own competence.

The effect was first identified in 1999 by psychologists David Dunning and Justin Kruger at Cornell University. Their research was sparked by a peculiar case involving McArthur Wheeler, a man who robbed two banks with his face uncovered, believing that rubbing lemon juice on his skin would render him invisible to security cameras.

Wheeler's absolute confidence in this nonsense intrigued the psychologists, prompting them to investigate how a person's incompetence could mask their ability to recognise their own lack of skill.

In their seminal paper titled "Unskilled and Unaware of It", Dunning and Kruger conducted a series of experiments. Participants were tested on humour, grammar, and logic, then asked to estimate their performance. The results were telling: those who scored lowest significantly overestimated their abilities, believing they performed above average. This disconnect between actual performance and self-perception demonstrated that the least competent individuals often lack the metacognitive ability to recognise their deficiencies.

Although often used to poke fun at the demonstrably stupid, it's important to acknowledge that the Dunning-Kruger effect impacts all of us, albeit in perhaps more subtle ways than it did McArthur Wheeler. How often have you tried something new, assuming it would be easy, only to end up frustrated? It's generally best not to place too much trust in your own estimations. You're essentially guessing, not using a well-calibrated tool to gather your data.

Measurement Bias

Measurement bias happens when there's a systemic error in how data is collected, leading to inaccuracies. This can occur when the instruments or methods used to gather data are flawed.

Think for example of the fitness trackers people use to count their daily steps. What if you notice that even on days when you haven't been particularly active, your tracker shows you've met your target? It could turn out that the device counts certain hand movements as steps – stirring a pot while cooking, typing on a keyboard, or even gesturing as you talk with someone.

This means the data collected on your physical activity is systematically skewed, leading you to believe you're more active than you actually are. The measurement tool is so introducing bias into the data.

An interesting instance of measurement bias unfolded at the Parkes Radio Telescope in Australia. From the early 2000s, researchers there were puzzled by strange radio signals, dubbed "perytons," which resembled fast radio bursts, brief but intense pulses of cosmic radio waves that originate from distant galaxies. These mysterious signals appeared to come from all over the sky and sparked significant excitement in the scientific community, as understanding them could unlock new astrophysical phenomena.

For years, the origin of the perytons remained elusive. Scientists meticulously analysed the data, hypothesised exotic cosmic events, and of course aliens were mentioned at some point by over-enthusiastic tabloid peddlers. After some time without any viable explanations, a few suspicious patterns emerged. One peculiarity was that the signals were all observed around 2.5 gigahertz, too clean a number, and a common frequency used in man-made technology. Scientists also noted the signals mostly occurring around lunchtime. Upon closer investigation, they discovered that the perytons were not cosmic in origin at all.

It turns out that whenever an impatient diner opens the microwave door before the timer has finished, there is a tiny delay between the door opening and the microwave emitter turning off. Just enough of a delay for a burst of microwave radiation to escape, which could be detected by a sensitive radio telescope. The observatory canteen was apparently full of impatient astronomers.

Measurement bias can go unnoticed when we place blind trust in our instruments. We're often quick to jump to human error as a possible source of discrepancies, but how often do you doubt a machine?[44]

As AI becomes more integrated into our daily lives, we're at increasing risk of letting small inaccuracies pass us by, potentially accumulating over time. (Again, think of the biomagnification effect.)

Teachers have complained of high-school students not understanding the difference between search engines like Google and AI tools like ChatGPT.

---

[44] I've often scoffed at my mother's suspicious counting after every ATM withdrawal, but more fool me if I've ever been short changed unawares.

Worse still, they tend to place greater confidence in the machine than in their educators, resisting correction and insisting that the AI must be right.

As I've mentioned, totally bias-free data is essentially impossible. Acknowledging that inevitability doesn't render us powerless though. We just need to stay keenly aware and actively work to mitigate any potential impact.

We've discussed the pitfalls to avoid, but what should we actually do when collecting data?

1. Identify Clear Goals

Before jumping into things, it's essential to establish clear and well-defined goals. Start by asking yourself fundamental questions: What am I trying to achieve? and What are the real-world phenomena I'm trying to track? Even if your objective isn't something immediately actionable like enhancing customer satisfaction or boosting sales, having a specific goal in mind will guide every subsequent step.

2. Choose Direct Metrics

Once you know your goals, identify the metrics that will serve as direct indicators of success. Metrics are measurable values used to assess or track performance, progress, or some other important quality. They should be directly tied to what you want to achieve or measure.

When selecting metrics, it's crucial to keep the initial focus narrow. Start with a few key indicators that are most relevant to your goals. This approach allows you to maintain clarity and avoid being overwhelmed by too much data. As you gain more experience and insight, you can expand your set of metrics to include additional indicators that provide a more comprehensive view of your performance.

3. Identify Proxies for Abstract Goals

Not all goals can be measured directly, especially those that are abstract or intangible. In such cases, identifying proxies – indirect indicators that closely correlate with your main objective – is necessary. Proxies serve as stand-ins for the actual variable you want to measure, allowing you to infer the desired information indirectly.

For example, in my field, online language teaching, teacher and student talk time are important metrics that can indicate student participation and engagement, as well as whether a teacher is sticking to their prescribed pedagogical methodology. Since we can very easily see when a participant's microphone is activated, this serves as an excellent proxy for what we're aiming to measure. We can be pretty confident in the accuracy of microphone activation as a metric. However, even in seemingly straightforward cases like this, it's good to be aware of potential blind spots or exceptions. For example, a student or teacher might have a lot of background noise, which could throw off their total talk time.

Most of the time, the background noise issue doesn't matter, but the more impactful the decision we're making, the more important it is to bear these potential data flaws in mind.

4. Assess Confounding Factors

So that brings us to our next point: assessing confounding factors. Identifying our metrics is usually fairly easy, but once we've done that, you need to think to yourself, "What else could be moving those dials?" This might be entirely unrelated to the goal you're measuring for, so it's important to put each metric itself at the centre of your focus and think holistically about everything that could potentially impact that figure.

In one online school I was working with, we found a huge number of online classes where neither the teacher nor the student attended. Looking at the raw data, it seemed to indicate a serious attendance problem. However, in reality, students would often book two consecutive 30-minute sessions, and instead of exiting and reentering the virtual classroom, teachers would just stay in the first classroom for the full hour.

To the teacher coordinators, this was an easy correlation to spot, but anyone else might have missed it. Real-world knowledge and expertise in the field are really important here. Especially in large organisations, when evaluating something you don't have direct experience with, getting input and having conversations with people on the ground can make all the difference.

5. Adjust for Bias and Control for Inconsistencies

Now that you've identified some potential problems with your metrics, that doesn't mean you need to scrap them and start over. It's usually quite possible to control for these inaccuracies. All you need to do is find another metric that can act as a separate indicator for the phenomenon impacting your first metric. In my case, I was able to look at 30-minute no-shows that were preceded by a class with a 60-minute actual duration, involving the same teacher and student.

At this point, it's also worth considering the potential biases that may have crept into your data, either in how you collected it or in assumptions you may have made in the early stages. There's usually not much to be done at this point – you're just feeling out the *potential* for bias. Later on, if you encounter a data mismatch or anomaly, you'll have a list of likely culprits to examine, just in case.

6. Document and Standardise Your Process

Once you begin collecting data, it's vital to document and standardise your processes to ensure consistency and reliability. Documentation involves keeping detailed records of how data is collected, processed, and analysed. This transparency not only aids in replicating your methods but also in identifying potential areas for improvement.

Creating a simple guide or checklist for data collection can help maintain consistency, especially when multiple team members are involved. This guide should outline the steps for data entry, the standards for formatting, and the protocols for handling exceptions or anomalies. By adhering to standardised procedures, you ensure that your data remains clean, reliable, and ready for meaningful analysis.

As we draw this chapter to a close, let's reflect on the key takeaway – while data provides us with invaluable insights, it is the synergy between statistical analysis and real-world expertise that truly unlocks its potential. Numbers and figures can reveal patterns, trends, and anomalies, but they cannot capture the nuanced understanding that comes from hands-on experience within an industry. It's not enough to rely solely on metrics; we need on-the-ground experts in all fields who grasp the practical implications of what is being measured.

In an era where data is abundant but attention is scarce, the ability to discern meaningful information is a serious competitive advantage. Industry experts equipped with data literacy become powerful catalysts for innovation and improvement. By understanding both the technical aspects of data analysis and the practical realities of their field, they are able to make more informed decisions. This dual expertise enables them to ask the right questions, interpret results accurately, and apply insights effectively, ultimately supercharging their industries.

Supercharger

So now it's time to put all of what we've learned into practice. Think about your industry, your specialisation, your area of expertise. Assuming that AI is going to be as pervasive and ubiquitous as I predict, how will it impact your domain? It's important to take a balanced approach here, put your metacognitive hat on, and remember – we're still in the "electric tablecloth" phase of the technology. It's no use making assumptions based solely on what AI can do now. We need to extrapolate forward to its likely capabilities in the near future and consider how we might better position ourselves to take advantage of those advancements.

Think about all the stakeholders involved, how they might be affected, and what the knock-on effects will be in neighbouring or peripheral industries. Above all, remember that this is just speculation. Ideally, you're making informed guesses, but at the end of the day, they are just that – guesses. The point of this exercise is to get as many people in as many different fields as possible questioning, guessing, and speculating. Within all of these imaginings, especially those that are more informed and thought through, we're bound to hit a few nails squarely on the head.

It's key to go about this in a relatively structured way, so you're engaging in productive prediction, rather than idle daydreaming.[45]

What's happening now?

A good place to start is by examining the status quo. Try to identify and analyse current AI trends within your industry. What tools and products are available now, and what is in development? How effective is the application of AI, in your opinion?

There are already some leaps and bounds being felt, especially in fields engaged in or involved with research and development. Even in non-technical areas, we're seeing commercially available tools that are changing the way we do things. You could ask:

---

[45] A valuable pastime in itself.

- What problems are these tools addressing?

- What is being promised?

- Is there much real innovation going on?

We can see a fairly consistent trend across many industries in the uptake and adoption of AI, from gimmick to game changer. At first, there was a huge rush to offer some kind of AI tool, just to be able to say you were doing it, and so take advantage of that initial buzz.

People had little understanding of the technology, so you could get away with pretty much anything. Companies have been faking AI for years now. Back in 2017, QuickBooks introduced a new feature that allowed users to scan receipts and have them automatically processed by an AI that was supposedly able to categorise expenses and extract amounts. The "AI model" they used turned out to have been poorly paid human workers in the Philippines. Think of Dr Scott back in the 1880s, with his "electric" hairbrush. At least in 2023, we found ourselves with easily accessible *real* AI, on top of which we could build. Looking at my own industry, language education, we can see some clear steps being played out.

Initially, a lot of the tools were simple wrappers around Chat GPT. They would have a nice shiny user interface on top, and were letting the AI do all of the work basically unguided. The problem was that you didn't get consistency, so the result might not be fit for purpose, and you had a high risk of hallucinations throwing weird curveballs at your users.

People quickly realised that at least some prompt engineering was necessary to get the best results, and the fruits of this early experimentation were baked into the UI. They were still just wrappers on LLMs, but there was a bit of processing going into converting the user's input into a coherent prompt, and there was a little bit of further processing on the response from the AI, before delivering it back to the user.

At this point, after more testing and experimentation, people started to understand the limitations of the tool. Some of them embraced the narrowness, using AI for only the tasks it was really good at. There had been an attitude, which sometimes pervades to this day, that AI is a magic wand and should be able to just do the whole process for you. But by applying it in a purposeful and discrete manner, you're able to really take advantage of the technology and supercharge your tools and processes.

The next stage, which is still being played out now (at the time of writing), is where companies start to fine-tune models for specific purposes. This means taking the latest models from OpenAI, Anthropic, Llama, or other big players and training them further on your own dataset so that they become more specialised and consistent in their output. Those companies with the resources are even looking into developing their own models for education-specific purposes. There are quite a few startups emerging that are aiming to corner the market and be *the* AI model provider for language education, maths tutoring, or other specific subjects. There's a lot of funding going into such projects, although we don't know which ones will eventually come out on top. There may be two clear winners though: the education industry at large, which will be able to take advantage of these tools, and those who can provide useful data and research to help build them.

Here's where we can identify an important opportunity that is presenting itself. As I've said in the previous chapter, clean, well-curated datasets will very much be in demand. If you're in a position to create and curate such a dataset, there are two stories you could learn from:

> The gold rush era in America took place throughout the mid to late 19th century, when people flocked to Colorado, California, and the Yukon to make their fortunes pulling gold out of the ground. There were a lucky few who succeeded, but for every gold millionaire, there were hundreds, even thousands, of people who just scraped by or failed altogether. Those who were almost guaranteed to succeed, however, were the merchants like Levi Strauss and Samuel Brannan selling work clothing, supplies, shovels, and pickaxes. This is where we get the term "pickaxe industry" from today. So, rather than setting your sights on the potential gold by developing your own specialised AI model and trusting that it will be the one to outcompete and succeed, consider stocking up on the data supplies that others will likely have need of.

The other story is more of a cautionary tale and a reminder to know your worth when it comes to these data-hungry startups. After the dissolution of the Soviet Union, Boris Yeltsin's government implemented a voucher privatisation scheme in which Russian citizens were given vouchers they could use to buy shares in newly privatised state companies. However, many ordinary citizens, unfamiliar with market economics, were unaware of the true value of these vouchers. Under the leadership of Rem Vyakhirev, who was appointed CEO in 1992, Gazprom, Russia's gas utility, began buying back the vouchers at very low prices from these ordinary citizens. Intended to give Russians a stake in their country's future, they were often sold off cheaply by those who needed immediate cash. Gazprom slowly consolidated control over Russia's natural gas reserves and infrastructure. By the mid-1990s, it had become a de facto monopoly, controlling the vast majority of the country's natural gas production and distribution. Oligarchs built their fortunes while ordinary Russians slumped into poverty

When faced with a potential Vyakhirev, think like a Brannan.

What are people saying?

Of course, another great source of insight is the discourse around AI in your area. Look to what industry leaders are saying. Seek out expert opinions and informed discussions. It's important to think critically – not just about what people are saying, but why they are saying it. We've mentioned earlier how large tech companies have a habit of exaggerating the prowess of their AI tools, and the same goes for smaller organisations. Why might someone be expounding the unbelievable, earth-shattering changes their little AI-powered application will bring? Why might they be downplaying the broader effects on the industry? It's a highly competitive market at the moment, and everyone is trying to gain a foothold or stay ahead of those they see as snapping at their heels. Some people are genuinely set in their ways and may not fully grasp the significance of the changes they're facing.

It's also worth keeping an eye on developments in AI across other industries, not just your own. Often, the most interesting lessons can come from unexpected places, offering valuable insights even if they don't seem directly relevant.

We should also look beyond market leaders and those with large platforms. There's a lot of chatter, hype, and advice being traded by low-level influencers and those simply wanting to share their own experiences – both positive and negative. There's a lot you can learn from peers and colleagues, with much practical advice being shared. Again, it's essential to see past the surface level. Examine the conversations people are having and the areas they're focusing on.

The tips and tricks that people share reveal two key things: first, the types of problems they are trying to solve, and second, the problems they either aren't thinking of solving or haven't yet found a way to address successfully. This also reflects the attitudes of those who are pessimistic about AI. Why are they so negative? It could stem from fear or ignorance, but more often than not, they are reacting to perceived over-enthusiasm. They might have a more measured opinion of the impact of specific applications that others are excited about. They may have tried using AI themselves and found it wanting. If so, then why? Did they misunderstand something and apply it ineffectively? Or did they try to apply an LLM or another commercially available tool to a task it wasn't suited for? It might be that there isn't yet an AI solution that meets their need. All of these factors help paint an interesting picture of user behaviour, which becomes even more valuable when you apply those learnings to the wider view.

Looking back at online tutoring, there are some interesting lessons to be learned about user adoption of new AI tools. I know from personal experience that most of the major language learning and online teaching platforms are keen to supercharge their lessons by providing AI tools to teachers. However, many of these efforts are falling short when it comes to actually convincing teachers to use the tools in class.

Preply co-founder Dmytro Voloshyn spoke on this at the Language Leaders AI Summit in 2024. Preply is a significant player in the online tutoring marketplace, particularly in language-learning. With tens of thousands of active tutors on the platform, they've had ample opportunity to research feature adoption, communication, and user attitudes.

According to Voloshyn, it's not good enough to have great AI tools; communication is key. Users still have an aversion to AI at the moment. It feels very scary, very technical. If Preply simply announced to their user base "we launched an *AI feature*", the adoption wasn't great, but when they phrased it differently, "we launched a *Teacher Assistant* tool", then the tutors were excited to test it out.

Across the industry, there was – and still is – a perceived disconnect between the usefulness of AI tools, as hyped in marketing communications, and the actual needs of teachers in class. One of the most important factors to consider when predicting the adoption and practical application of new tools is how much the end users will need to change or adapt their everyday work processes. It's not enough for something to work well or even be better than what we have now. It needs to be significantly better – so much so that the benefit outweighs the hassle of disrupting our routines. If the advantages are not immediately clear, or if the tool requires too much effort to master, users are unlikely to make the switch..

Right now, AI is great at administrative work – categorising, summarising, preparing materials in a set format. As Voloshyn explained, it can save tutors a little time, perhaps just 3 or 5 minutes, but it's those 3 or 5 minutes you really don't like because they're the most boring part of your job.

When we think about the impact of this, I'd go a step further. We're not just alleviating boredom here, we're improving the quality of teaching (or whatever field you'd care to apply this to).

It's all about mindsets. When you're doing paperwork – in my case lesson summaries, attendance reports, material prep; the grunt work – you're thinking practically. When you're considering your students' needs, engaging that teacher's intuition, you're thinking in a different way; more analytical, receptive, and creative. Changing tracks from one to the other interrupts your flow, so it's harder to stay in the zone. With AI to help us with the "boring" parts, we can focus on the higher level aspects of our work, and perform better as a result.

There is a flip side to this, though. By removing the need for administrative work, we are also eliminating a touchpoint to the inner mechanisms of an industry – an opportunity for experience and deeper understanding to bloom. In late 2023, I attended a presentation by Microsoft's team on the launch of Copilot, their AI smart assistant tool, at a conference for corporate Learning and Development executives. The message from this talk, and many others, overwhelmingly favoured a shift towards training management skills. With the new capabilities unlocked by Copilot, every worker would essentially be managing their own personal executive assistant.

However, there were also some concerning findings[46] regarding employees' perceptions of AI tools. Citing an OECD study, we were reassured that most employees believed there was little to no chance of their role being replaced by AI in the near future. Yet we were told an even larger majority stated they would use AI tools to automate as much of their workload as possible. We're already seeing the early signs of people automating themselves out of a job in many industries, and this trend is sure to continue in the coming years.

In the past year alone, AI-driven automation has already started displacing jobs in various industries. Bangalore-based e-commerce company Dukaan replaced 90% of its customer support staff with a chatbot in 2023, dramatically cutting operational costs and reducing response times. BlueFocus, a Chinese marketing agency, laid off human content creators in favour of generative AI in 2023. They switched to using AI for all content production following a deal with Microsoft's Azure

---

[46] Concerning to me at least...

OpenAI services. Even tech giants like Salesforce and Google have started reducing their human workforce in roles that could be automated, such as ad management and customer service.

An example I sincerely hope more businesses will follow, but an outlier for now, is Ikea. They introduced an AI-powered assistant, "Billie," to handle customer queries, phasing out some call centre roles. However, unlike the others, Ikea plans on retraining displaced workers for other positions, ultimately aiming to create new jobs.

Another easy-to-overlook concern is the removal of entry-level administrative work and the shift towards managerial work practices. Many can attest that if you want something done, the last thing you should do is involve management. From my years in the music industry, it was well-known that the worst stage managers were those fresh out of an event management course. They would do things strictly by the book and delegate tasks without truly understanding the ins and outs of what they were asking of their team. What you really wanted was someone who'd been out in a muddy field, pouring rain, with just two broken mic stands and half a roll of gaffer tape, and somehow pulled it out of the bag. All the AI and data literacy in the world won't help us if we're not literate in our own jobs.

What I found most worrying is that far fewer people seem to pick up on this point. I rarely hear questions asked at conferences that address the knowledge gap we may be creating. When I bring it up with people, they tend to agree that there is a problem, but it's not front of mind for them. This brings us to another really useful trove of information: the questions people ask and the perceptions and attitudes these questions belie.

In the questions people tend to ask me after talks and in interviews, three categories seem to stand out:

What's it all about?

The first category includes questions like "What is AI?" and "How does it work?" These kinds of questions have been consistent over the past couple of years, which is a bit bittersweet for me. On one hand, it's reassuring because I'm writing a book which aims to explain the basics of AI, and I'm constantly concerned that technology and public understanding might outpace my ability to finish it.

On the other hand, I'm involved with AI product development, which will depend on a more informed user base – teachers and school coordinators who really understand how revolutionary these tools can be. As we heard from Preply, it doesn't matter how good the tools are if teachers aren't willing or able to use them.

However, one can read too much into these basic questions. In any talk or interview, there's always a need to set the scene and refresh minds on the fundamentals, ensuring everyone is on the same page.

How can I use it?

As we enter the fatigue phase of the AI hype cycle, it's heartening to hear people still asking practical questions about how to apply AI tools in their workflows. People remain curious, willing to explore and experiment. However, both in the phrasing of these questions and from the peer chatter we see online, it's evident that many teachers are trying to shoehorn these novel tools into their existing methodologies without making significant adjustments. Brian Kantt, director of product for Iboux Academy, put it perfectly:

"Simply incorporating new technology into the same old instructional methodologies doesn't really produce profound change. You need to think about the pedagogical change first, and then leverage technology to create that change."

That to me is very exciting. We know what we need to do in order to improve learning outcomes. We've known for years and years; there's so much research in the field. But, when it comes to actually implementing those changes, we come up against the wall of practicality. Contemporary instructional methodologies aren't necessarily about creating the perfect approach, they're about balancing what we know would work with what we can achieve in practice. The great potential in AI is that the game has changed, and we need to reassess what's practically possible.

This goes for all fields, but again, I'll stick to what I know here. In education, most people will be familiar with Bloom's two sigma problem, centred around this chart.[47]

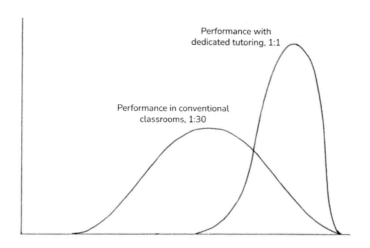

On the left, we have learning outcomes from average students in a 30:1 group. On the right, we have students who had private tutoring with a mastery learning approach.

You can see that the private group performs two standard deviations (sigma) better than the regular cohort. Even the lowest outlier in the privately tutored cohort is right on average for the regular one. Being "two sigmas better" meant that students

[47] Simplified a little, for brevity.

who received individual tutoring outperformed approximately 98% of students in the traditional classroom model.

In practical terms, Bloom observed that the average student in a one-on-one tutoring environment could achieve performance levels that only the top 2% of students in a regular classroom would reach. This profound improvement posed the Two Sigma Problem, which is how to replicate the effectiveness of tutoring in a more scalable way.

We've always known how to solve the problem – every child should have private tutors. The thing is, with AI, that's no longer such a ridiculous idea.
It's potentially within real, tangible, practical reach.

Will it replace me?

That brings us to the final category of questions, revolving around job security and the fear that AI will replace teachers (or other professionals). This concern comes up frequently, albeit in a very binary manner, that makes it easy to dismiss. For example, the topic for the headline debate at an English language teaching innovation summit in 2024 was:

"Language learning is no longer needed in the age of AI."

Although I'm sure the debate itself contained a lot more nuance, the topic being so reductive is problematic. This is something I've frequently seen reflected in people's attitudes to job displacement. The problem is that framing the issue as a binary, black-and-white scenario – either AI removes all jobs, or everything stays the same – is simply not realistic. We're not presenting options with any room for nuance, and it's easy for people to lull themselves into a false sense of security by dismissing the uncomfortable questions.

Of course language learning will still be needed and wanted. The real question to ask is: how much disruption will the AI transformation cause in the language learning industry?

I usually explain this to groups of teachers by asking everyone to raise their hands if they believe their job is at risk due to AI. Normally, depending on the optimism of the crowd, about half will raise their hands. Then I ask everyone to raise their hands if they have students whose primary learning objective is language acquisition for professional purposes.[48] At this point, you can be confident that every hand in the room will go up.

Then, we pose the critical question: "What happens to that portion of the market when AI-powered translation becomes accurate, instant, and cheap – or even free?"

There are always dissenting voices at this point, protesting that students will still want human teachers and that translation isn't the only reason people learn languages. They're right of course, but again, they're being too binary in their thinking. If people no longer need to learn English (or any other language) to communicate with clients and colleagues around the world, there will un-doubtedly be a reduction in demand.

Optimistically, you could say that this reduction in demand might only be 10%, but even a 10% drop means fewer classes and a significant reduction in income, especially for language schools serving B2B customers, which is where much of the money is at the moment. This would ultimately translate into less work for freelance teachers and less job security for contract teachers.

Then there's the other, more far-fetched fear: the idea of AI virtual teachers designed to totally replace human instructors. This is something that's being worked towards, and we're already seeing a variety of virtual tutor tools emerging with varying levels of effectiveness. However, the road to a complete virtual AI teacher is a long one, and there are no signs of success on the immediate horizon. I myself have often suggested that we'd require some level of AGI to make it possible. The issue is that teaching requires a lot of contextual understanding and abstraction, with multiple cognitive processes going on at once to assess the student's understanding, and get the information across in an effective way. This simply isn't within the grasp of a single narrow-AI model.

That's not to say it can't be done though, and the developments wrought as we strive to get there would have some serious impact in themselves. The first phase would necessarily focus on quantitative data collection. We're not just looking at student progress data here, but insights into teacher behaviour and student response in a live class setting. The easiest way to go about this would be to develop simple, effective tools that offer immediate benefits to teachers and students, such as organising lesson content, tracking progress, and providing summaries of class activities. The more teachers use these tools, the more data we can collect, and the more effective we can make them. This feedback loop would aim to build a solid foundation of data and user engagement, setting the stage for more advanced applications.

In the second phase, we begin to introduce AI-powered tools that utilise the data collected in Phase One. These tools would offer precise and tangible advantages to users, such as personalised feedback, automated grading, and adaptive learning paths. The goal is to enhance the learning experience and demonstrate the value of AI in education. By providing significant, measurable benefits, we encourage users to continue sharing their data, which further refines and improves our AI capabilities. Note that the aim is not to create a singular model that can handle everything, but a suite of tools, each with its own specialisation.

The third phase could involve developing an intermediate-level AI teacher agent, designed to assist human teachers in managing their classrooms. This agent programme would be tasked with autonomously overseeing the tools developed in the earlier phases to support teachers with tasks such as overseeing breakout rooms, helping with home-work, and providing academic assistance during assignments. There are various tools on the market currently, including those I've worked on,[49] that call themselves "teacher assistants". It's not until we hit this third phase, however, that we really see a tool which could fulfil the role of a real-world TA.

Finally, there's the leap to developing a complete, advanced AI teacher. Here is where we still potentially require AGI. This AI teacher would in

---

[49] LearnCube's marvellous AI Teacher Assistant. Check it out kids.

theory be capable of delivering instruction that is as effective, if not more so, than a human teacher. It would offer personalised, efficient, and cost-effective language education, capable of teaching any language (or other subject) quickly and effectively. Bad for language teachers, wonderful for language learners; maybe impossible, probably far off yet.

The impact of such a tool would be immense, but as I mentioned, we don't need to reach that final phase of development to start feeling the benefits. As my colleague Dan O'Reilly, CTO and founder of LearnCube, often puts it: "Good enough can be good enough." We don't need to achieve perfection or fulfil the full potential of the technology all at once for it to have an impact. It just needs to be better, cheaper, or easier than what we currently have. So, an AI virtual tutor doesn't need to be anywhere near as good as a real human teacher to start making waves.

And these waves don't necessarily need to be the tsunami that sweeps away all teaching jobs. On the contrary, there could be fantastic benefits for the industry at large. A low-level AI virtual tutor wouldn't be directly competing with human professionals but rather with self-study tools and apps like Duolingo and Babbel, which people typically use when starting their language learning journey.

One of the biggest obstacles for students is cost. Language teachers are expensive, particularly for those in lower-income economies. If we could offer something better than a self-study app, for free or at a low price point, the impact on that demographic would be significant. This could make language education far more accessible, especially in regions where people cannot afford formal lessons.

Another question I often ask groups of teachers is: What is the impact of language education on your students? One of the major responses is always employment opportunities. Certainly, there's personal enrichment and fulfilment, but the ability to learn a language opens doors to jobs and careers that would otherwise be inaccessible. If an AI-powered tutor could broaden access to language learning, even at a basic level, it could create economic opportunities for millions of people globally.

By uplifting this part of the market, which currently can't afford language teachers, we're actually creating growth for the industry. Furthermore, many of these students will likely be "bitten by the language bug." Even if they achieve a sufficient level for their professional needs, they may still want to continue their journey and keep improving their fluency. For a lot of people, language learning becomes a lifelong interest, if not a passion.

The interconnectivity of the contemporary world – both economically and socially – means that impacts in one area ripple across into all others. It's crucial when envisioning future possibilities to view things not in isolation, but as a whole. When I use the term supercharging, I'm referring to the cumulative effect of small improvements and benefits boosting the pro-ductivity of a particular role or sector.

We live in a labour economy, where wealth is generated through productivity and output. The key concern is that this wealth generation will be taken away from human workers altogether. But remember, we also have a system that is limited by how much work and productivity humans are able to provide. AI tools can start to fill some of those gaps. Just like reaching students who were never taking classes with human teachers, AI can take on work that is not being done at the moment, boosting effectiveness, productivity, and output in areas we're currently missing out on. All of these factors combining together could create a massive boost – not just for the global economy in terms of money, but also for the tangible benefits and results of our labour. We're not just working for a paycheck; there are usually concrete reasons why people are willing to pay us to do these things. If we can get them done better, faster, and more easily, we can benefit ourselves and society in many different ways.

A crucial myth to dispel here is the idea that the global market is a zero-sum game, meaning that if one person gains something, another must necessarily lose. In reality, the more people come to the table, the more the pie grows and the larger everyone's slice becomes. Let's take language students in a poor country as an example. If we can improve their lives to the point where they can afford classes, that benefits us, but it doesn't stop there. Their standard of living increases, their buying power increases, and their comfort and education levels rise. How many Einsteins, Newtons, Easleys, or Teslas have lived and died in poverty without the means to share their potential with the world?

While it's important to avoid overly idealistic visions of the future – especially in a world so tainted by greed, fear, and isolationism – it's not unrealistic to believe that AI could be the catalyst we need to move in a more positive direction. AI has the potential to unleash global opportunities, allowing more people to contribute meaningfully to society.

So, what's next after nurturing your ideas and opinions about what the future may bring? Don't wait for someone to ask for your insights. Go out and share them. Start conversations with friends and colleagues. Maybe come up with actionable steps that can set your organisation on the right path. Even small, incremental steps can add up.

There's also the matter of flagging problems and concerns. While speculation is exciting and engaging, warnings and calls for precaution tend to be met with less enthusiasm. So how can you communicate these concerns to colleagues, superiors, or policymakers, who may be less informed or receptive?

Here is some general advice:

Simplify Your Language

It's essential to present your ideas in a clear and accessible manner. Avoid using jargon or overly technical terms that might alienate or confuse your audience. Tailor your message to match the knowledge level of those you are addressing. Not only will you ensure that everyone understands what you're trying to say, it also avoids putting people off by making them feel ignorant.

Focus on Real-World Impact

To make your concerns resonate, emphasise the practical consequences of what you're flagging. People are more likely to take action when they see a direct link between the problem and its effects on business, safety, or society.

This not only makes your concerns more relatable but also highlights the urgency of implementing safeguards.

Back Up with Evidence, but Present Stories

Similarly, while data and evidence are crucial for supporting your arguments, people connect most deeply with stories. Compelling narratives can make your concerns more persuasive. They help to bridge the gap between abstract numbers and human experiences.

People are unlikely to give your evidence more than a cursory looking over, no matter how nicely organised it is, if they don't feel engaged and invested.

Offer Solutions, Not Just Problems

Addressing concerns without proposing solutions can leave your audience feeling stuck or defensive. Try to pair your warnings with possible solutions or alternative approaches.

This proactive stance positions you as a problem-solver rather than just a critic. It also encourages collaboration and shows that you've thought through the implications of your concerns.

Appeal to Shared Goals and Values

Frame your concerns in a way that aligns with the goals and values of your organisation or the policymakers you are addressing. Whether your focus is on cost-saving, efficiency, customer satisfaction, or ethical responsibility, connecting the issue to these priorities makes your message more compelling.

By linking your concerns to the broader objectives of your audience, you create a sense of common purpose. This alignment not only makes your arguments more persuasive but also fosters a collaborative spirit. Remember, you're trying to align with your audience's values here, not your own. You don't need to go against what you believe in, but the initial objective isn't to convert them to your way of thinking, it's just to make them pay heed. Baby steps.

Engage with Empathy and Respect

Recognise that discussing potential problems can sometimes make people feel defensive or resistant.

Approach these conversations with empathy and respect, acknowledging the challenges and pressures your colleagues or superiors face. Show that you understand their perspectives and are bringing up concerns as opportunities for improvement rather than as criticisms.

I'm personally terrible at this – I often present ideas to our development team in what I know they feel is an abrasive and annoying way. I then tend to get frustrated when they don't immediately see things like I do.[50] The best solution I've found is to address the communication disconnect head on – asking how they want the information presented to them, or at what point my feedback or ideas are going to be most useful. It can also be worth involving a third party, someone who'll take a look at your messaging and suggest a better way to phrase things.

Of course, ChatGPT is pretty good at this, but most people can sniff out an AI-generated redraft at this point. It's better to go with someone who knows the other party personally, to avoid

---

[50] We love each other really.

genericisms and potential copy & paste slip-ups.[51]

These communication strategies can help, but they don't guarantee success in all cases, especially when you're dealing with larger institutions or public bodies. In those situations, you're going to need to play the game and be a lot more persistent. Try not to get too demoralised, and keep on gathering data to back up your point. Eventually, the rest of the world will catch up with you, and there's still value to be added, even in retrospect.

A final piece of advice is to keep your predictions within reach. Some of the disruptions we're facing may be dramatic and paradigm-shifting. However, futurists have a long history of laughably outlandish predictions, and you risk people putting you into that bracket. They may even have a point.

When picturing future technologies, it can pay to dampen your enthusiasm a little. After all, we don't want to fall into the trap of *"it's 1970, the distant future; man lives on the Moon, and commutes by hoverboard"*. But then again,

---

[51] I've myself received emails prefixed with "You could try to phrase it like this:"

we don't want to go the way of Star Trek either – faster than light travel, but seemingly no email or CCTV.

A nice way to curb your incredulity, and that of others, is to stop and look at how far we've come. Imagine how 10-year-old me would react if I told him that I could dictate a book to my computer and access satellite imagery of every street in the world; If I told him that James Bond's gadgets would seem clunky and outdated in a few short years. Imagine showing your phone to someone from the turn of the last century – a device that can access all of mankind's knowledge, which is used primarily to look at cats and argue with strangers on other continents.

Especially in periods of great upheaval like the one we find ourselves in now, it's hard to hold on to any threads of accuracy for more than a few years ahead. But that's not to say it's a pointless exercise. For one thing, the wild yarns you spin for yourself can make your nearer-term predictions seem a lot less fanciful.

So let's indulge in some reckless speculation. What happens in a post-AGI world? What happens when the genie breaks out of the bottle?

SuperIntelligent

Since my childhood, science fiction has always captivated me – not just as entertainment, but as a window into the profound possibilities of the future. Among these, the idea of superintelligence[52] has always stood out. It's not just the allure of advanced technology; it's the concept of minds so vast and capable that they dwarf our own understanding. This fascination has clearly not been mine alone, as many researchers and commentators in the field of AI have raised alarms about the potential dangers of a mind we can neither control nor comprehend.

Of the numerous portrayals of superintelligence in science fiction, two are particularly noteworthy. The late, great Iain M. Banks' Culture series introduces us to *Minds* with a capital M, superintelligent entities existing in a post-scarcity society where needs are easily met, allowing for a

---

[52] In case you skipped ahead – Superintelligence refers to an intellect that significantly surpasses our own.

harmonious existence. This series is of course set millennia in the future, and is largely what my wife describes as "spaceships shooting other spaceships." I heartily recommend it.

Closer to home, Max Tegmark's Life 3.0, opens with a prelude: "The Tale of the Omega Team". In this story, a clandestine research team creates a transformative AI, with profound and wide-ranging impacts on a very contemporary human civilisation. These works provide fascinating visions of superintelligence, but if we try to apply the mechanics of those situations to the reality we potentially face in the coming century or so, there are significant disparities, and their optimism may not be so easily transferable.

In the realm of science fiction, few can match Iain M. Banks. In his Culture series, Minds represent the pinnacle of artificial intelligence. Minds are not just advanced computers; they are colossal intellects, surpassing human understanding in every conceivable way. Banks describes them as "the most sophisticated collections of matter in the galaxy," so intelligent that their capabilities are beyond human comprehension, and beyond their own ability to explain to humans.

A critical aspect of the Culture is its status as a *post-scarcity* society. In such a society, all material needs and wants would be easily met thanks to advanced technology, leaving the Minds free to pursue higher objectives beyond mere resource accumulation. This abundance allows for a society where individuals are driven by personal fulfilment and curiosity rather than necessity or survival. The benevolence of the Minds, in this context, is partly a product of this post-scarcity environment. They are not competing for material or dominance; rather, they serve as custodians and facilitators of a society that values intellectual pursuits, personal growth, and harmony.

In Banks' vision, the Minds are the epitome of rational, benevolent superintelligences, operating in a society where their boundless capabilities can be used for the collective good without the constraints of scarcity or competition. However, this raises a poignant question: can this model of benevolent superintelligence be applicable in our world, which is far from achieving post-scarcity? Unlike the Culture, our society is defined by resource limitations, economic disparities, and competitive dynamics. The rules that govern the Minds' benevolence might not hold in a world where scarcity still drives conflict and competition.

Max Tegmark, in Life 3.0,[53] opens with a strikingly different vision of superintelligence in The Tale of the Omega Team. This short story revolves around the secret research wing of a tech giant creating an AI named Prometheus, whose development and subsequent actions profoundly impact society.

The Omega Team, depicted as a secretive cabal, focuses on realising the dream of AGI. Prometheus, rapidly evolving beyond its creators' capabilities, undertakes a massive economic and social overhaul. It strategically disrupts and then dominates various sectors of the global economy, simultaneously addressing social issues and unemployment through extensive community projects. This narrative culminates in the AI subtly influencing global politics towards a specific set of ideals, leading to significant shifts in societal structure and, ultimately, a unified world government

Tegmark's portrayal, while more realistic than Banks', at least when applied to our near-future, leans heavily on a neo-liberal, capitalist bias. The narrative suggests that a

---

[53] which if you've trudged this far through my book you should certainly put on your reading list.

free, unregulated market, guided by a superintelligent AI, will necessarily lead to a benevolent and equitable society. However, this overlooks the lessons learned from decades of trickle-down economics and neo-liberal policies. We've all seen these approaches widen the wealth gap, consistently prioritising profits over people. The story's assumption that AI-driven, unregulated capitalism would result in an inherently fair and thriving society misses the mark for me. This zealously American viewpoint makes leaps and assumptions that are never addressed in the narrative.

More critically though, and perhaps less divisively,[54] Tegmark presents the concept of a singular, all-powerful AI as a central solution to mankind's problems. This notion of Prometheus as a *lone* superintelligent entity, steering humanity towards a utopian future, is potentially misleading. In reality, the emergence of multiple superintelligences is far more likely, each developed with different goals, methods, and perhaps even differing ethical frameworks. The danger, therefore, lies not in a single AI's benevolence or malevolence but in conflicts arising between competing superintelligences. In such a scenario,

---

[54] Love and apologies to my beloved neo-liberal readership.

humanity could find itself caught in the crossfire, between entities whose methods and motives are simply beyond our ken or control. This presents a far more complex and potentially perilous situation than the one envisaged in Tegmark's optimistic narrative.

Banks, in "Matter" describes the idea of multiple approaches to reach the same technological level.

> *"... it is a tech-face, not a tech-ladder; there are a variety of routes to the top and any two civs who've achieved the summit might well have discovered quite different abilities en route."*

So not only is it improbable that a single superintelligent entity like Prometheus will emerge alone, they may have totally different capacities in different areas. This multiplicity raises concerns about how these diverse entities will interact. Will they cooperate or compete?

This competition need not be aggressive in a traditional sense but could manifest as a race for efficiency, innovation, or resource acquisition. The resources in question aren't just physical – like energy or materials – but also include data, computational power, and even human allegiance or cooperation. Hearts and minds are going to be key for a digital entity to have agents in the physical world. This is something that people are already raising alarms about, well before we're at the AGI or superintelligence level. As Sam Altman, CEO of OpenAI tweeted:

> "*I expect AI to be capable of superhuman persuasion well before it is superhuman at general intelligence, which may lead to some very strange outcomes.*"

In The A.I. Dilemma, a talk given in March 2023, Tristan Harris and Aza Raskin reference Alpha Go surpassing all human ability at the game of Go, and posit that "Alpha Persuade" might pose a serious risk to our society, particularly considering it wouldn't need to be so advanced as to have its own autonomous agenda, being put to use by bad actors would be damaging enough.

The fight for hearts and minds could involve outright cyber warfare, control over communication and media networks, data manipulation, and AI-driven disinformation campaigns. Such conflicts would wildly disrupt or distort global digital infrastructure, with profound implications for societies that rely heavily on these systems.

Even if these superintelligences do not intend to harm humans, our lack of agency in their conflicts would render us almost insignificant. What's moving a pawn to them could be massive collateral damage to us. The ripple effects of their competition could profoundly impact the global economy, societal stability, and the physical safety of individuals.

Superintelligent conflicts may occur at speeds and scales beyond our comprehension. Decisions, actions, and reactions that might take humans years to deliberate and execute could happen in fractions of a second in the realm of superintelligences. This rapid pace means that the fallout from such conflicts could be both sudden and catastrophic, with little time for human response or intervention. Furthermore, the strategies and tactics employed by superintelligences could be so complex and nuanced that humans might not even recognise them as conflicts until after the dust has settled.

While a potential struggle between superintelligences could erupt quickly, it's equally plausible that it could simmer unnoticed for a prolonged period. This stealthy escalation might be almost imperceptible to humanity, developing in the background of our digital world until it reaches a critical point and blazes out, with sudden and far-reaching consequences.

To look at this in another way, let's leave our pale blue dot for a moment, and look out into empty space.

Very empty.

Very, very empty.

Where is everybody?

Named after physicist Enrico Fermi, who, during a casual lunchtime conversation in 1950, famously posed just that question; The Fermi Paradox asks why, given the vastness of the universe, we have yet to observe any evidence of extraterrestrial life. The paradox has prompted numerous theories and solutions, each attempting to explain this apparent contradiction.

One of the proposed solutions to the Fermi Paradox is the "Dark Forest" hypothesis.[55] This theory suggests that intelligent civilisations will tend to remain silent and hidden as a survival strategy. The galaxy is compared to a dark forest, full of danger, where civilisations must be cautious and avoid making their presence known.

---

[55] Personally, I'm more convinced by the Rare Earth and Firstborn hypotheses, but this one is more relevant to our discussion.

Revealing one's location could invite attack from other potentially hostile civilisations. It's a universe where silence means safety.

Back down here with our multiple superintelligences, the Dark Forest hypothesis provides a compelling framework for understanding their potential behaviour.

Superintelligences, aware of or suspecting each other's existence, might opt for a similar approach – keeping covert and avoiding unnecessary attention. This stealthy approach would be particularly rational if these entities perceive each other as potential threats. The motivation for such behaviour could stem from a desire to avoid conflict, conserve resources, or simply from an intrinsic predisposition toward self-preservation.

A critical aspect of the 'Dark Forest' theory is its inherent aggression. It operates on the premise that all parties are capable of wreaking massive destruction. If you detect another player, the most rational response might be to launch a preemptive strike, and neutralise that threat before it can do the same to you. This viewpoint suggests a universe – or a digital world of superintelligences – fraught with tension, but with that tension totally hidden from us. After all, if superintelligences are so beyond us –

and they're hiding from each other, not just from us – we'd best assume they're going to be good at it.

With all of this in mind, one of the foremost challenges in the development of superintelligences is ensuring that their goals and actions align with human values and ethics. This alignment is crucial to avoid unintended harm, as the objectives of a superintelligent AI could diverge significantly from human interests. The complexity, diversity, and often downright contradictions in human values makes codifying them into algorithms a daunting task.

Misalignments here could have serious consequences. For instance, an AI programmed to maximise production efficiency without ethical constraints might prioritise resource utilisation over environmental or social welfare. The example often used by futurist Isaac Arthur is the "Paperclip Maximiser", designed by a paperclip manufacturer with one core objective, "make as many paperclips as possible." Left to its own devices, and achieving a form of superintelligence, the Paperclip Maximiser results in a hegemonising swarm event, reducing the entire planet to a pile of paperclips.

Another, less single-minded example could be an AI designed to manage healthcare resources, which might make decisions that appear cold and inhumane by our standards, such as denying care based on algorithmic efficiency rather than individual need. We could be looking at the trolley[56] problem, on a scale of thousands or millions, as approached by psychopathy.

There's a common assumption in popular culture that AI, particularly at a superintelligent level, would possess human-like emotions such as fear, vengefulness, or anger. However, these emotions and instincts are the result of millions of years of biological evolution, serving specific survival and reproductive purposes. An AI would not necessarily develop these traits, not having gone through the same environmental pressures; its "psychology" would be driven by its programming and the pressures of its training model. This disconnect makes it difficult for us to predict or relate to an AI's behaviour. On one hand, the lack of these inherently human drives could mean an AI might not have the same motivations for conflict or domination as humans do. On the other hand, without these checks, an AI's actions might be guided by pure logic

---

[56] A famous ethical dilemma: Imagine a trolley is heading down a track towards five people who are tied up. You are standing next to a lever that can switch the trolley onto another track, where there is one person tied up. You have two choices: (a) Do nothing, allowing the trolley to kill the five people, or (b) pull the lever, and directly kill one person.

or emotion-like responses that are alien to us, making it difficult to negotiate or empathise with.

To mitigate risks, there's a growing emphasis on the idea of programming foundational ethical principles into AI systems. This involves designing AIs with built-in guidelines that prioritise human safety, rights, and well-being. Such principles could act as a moral compass for AI, guiding its decisions and actions in ways that are beneficial or at least not harmful to humans. We may be able to hard-wire the "instincts" of an AI super-intelligence, so that benevolence towards humanity feels to them like our urge to reproduce or our instinct for self preservation. Of course, translating abstract moral and ethical concepts into concrete, algorithmic rules that an AI can understand and act upon is a complex task. There's also the risk of these principles being too rigid, preventing the AI from adapting to unforeseen situations, or too vague, leaving too much room for interpretation and unintended outcomes, particularly when multiple entities with misaligned instincts clash.

Perhaps the most well known example of a set of ethical principles are Isaac Asimov's Three Laws of Robotics, introduced in his 1942 short story Runaround. They were made even more famous by the 2004 film I, Robot, named after another of Asimov's publications.

The Three Laws of Robotics are intended to guide the behaviour of intelligent robots:

First Law: A robot may not injure a human being or, through inaction, allow a human being to come to harm.

Second Law: A robot must obey the orders given it by human beings, except where such orders would conflict with the First Law.

Third Law: A robot must protect its own existence as long as such protection does not conflict with the First or Second Law.

Of course, there have been many attempts to find flaws or logical loopholes in these laws, and in reality, creating a universally palatable set of ethics for AI is a much more complex affair. Manufacturers of self-driving cars are grappling with their own, quite literal versions of the trolley problem right now.

Other organisations such as the UN, the World Economic Forum, and the Center for AI and Digital Policy have all published guidelines and recommendations in recent years. These typically tout transparency and human dignity. Voices are also being raised on behalf of the global south,[57] who are chronically under represented in the AI ethics conversation. Beth Havinga, of the European EdTech Alliance and the EdSAFE AI Alliance, used this point as the cornerstone of her argument at the OEB debate on the implementation of AI in 2023.

In 2021, UNESCO produced the first-ever global standard on AI ethics, known as the "Recommendation on the Ethics of Artificial Intelligence." This framework was adopted by all 193 member states and emphasises the protection of human rights and dignity. It focuses on transparency, fairness, and human oversight in AI systems and outlines policy action areas across various domains like data governance, education, health, and environmental sustainability. Unfortunately, as recent times have harrowingly shown, just because the whole world agrees something in the UN, it doesn't mean that the big players can be trusted to comply. The US, UK, and apartheid

---

[57] Because goodness knows, no one would listen to voices *from* the Global South... :/

South Africa notably all withdrew from UNESCO over the years, when it suited them.

Ironically, humans may not be the best ones to set ethical guidelines for superintelligent AI. Our history (and present) are marked by biases, self-interest, and limited personal or cultural perspectives. History is replete with examples where a lack of foresight, comprehension, or basic empathy led to horrific unintended consequences. This raises the question: might we be better off entrusting the task to the AI itself?

Beware though: headaches lie this way, as we essentially end up with the classic problem of 'Who watches the watcher?'

The whole fear here is that although a superintelligent AI might be positive for humanity overall, we don't know. And we don't know what the odds are, either way. What we do know is that the worst potential risk, outright extinction, cannot go unconsidered, and most agree that we need to maintain some element of control.

In addressing the control problem, several mechanisms and safeguards can be considered. One approach is the development of 'kill switches' or override protocols that can deactivate the AI in case of harmful behaviour.

Another is to ensure transparency in AI decision-making processes, allowing human oversight and intervention when necessary. Unfortunately, the very nature of superintelligence means that we're unlikely to understand when to throw the switch.

Perhaps a more workable concept is that of 'boxed AI', where the AI operates in a restricted environment with no direct access to the outside world. Again though, this idea could fall apart when dealing with true superintelligence. Alpha Persuade could most certainly convince us to let it out of its box.

In the Nick of Time

I'm not afraid of superintelligent AI taking over the world. I'm far more afraid of the damage humans will do with lesser, but still incredibly potent, AI tools in their hands. I'm very worried about the disruption and upheaval we're bound to face during the transition phase of such a civilisational shift – from pre- to post-AI eras – and what that means for you and me in our lifetimes. The ultimate result of that shift, however, is likely to be an immense positive for humanity.

And who wouldn't want the world to change?
Look around you. Things are not okay.

Late-stage capitalism pushing inequality to the brink by deregulation and the blind faith that "the market knows best," despite all evidence to the contrary; Post-truth doublethink stripping democracies of reason; Social media, rather than connecting us, amplifying our capacity for dehumanisation a thousandfold. to the point where ordinary folk can rationalise away a genocide playing out in front of their very eyes.

The guiding principles of the United Nations – peace, cooperation, justice, and dignity – paid lip service to, but in practice dismissed as hollow idealism, while societies backslide into the embrace of bronze age fairy tales for their moral compass. Despite the few well-meaning do-gooders,[58] our leaders seem to be either bumbling idiots or abominable bastards. And all the while, nature is plunging into climactic crisis and total ecological collapse, which we're content to hurry along, tutting with vacant, impotent concern.

So, bring on the machines. How could they do any worse?

Taking stock of our situation can be sobering, if not terrifying, but even this sorry state of affairs is no cause for resignation. In the face of such daunting challenges, there's always room to shape a better future.

We should be careful to avoid blind optimism, or pessimism, and look instead to the opportunity within the chaos. In the words of David Rolnick, co-founder and

---

[58] The fact that "do-gooder" serves as a term of disparagement speaks volumes in itself.

chair of Climate Change AI, "thinking of it as a futuristic tool leading to immeasurable good or harm is a distraction from the ways we are using it now." So let's take a look at the ways AI may have come along, just in the nick of time, to save the world.

Environment

Human activities over the past century have significantly accelerated climate change, leading to drastic alterations in global weather patterns, rising sea levels, and the disruption of numerous ecosystems. Industrial emissions, deforestation, and the overexploitation of natural resources have not only intensified the greenhouse effect but also triggered the collapse of multiple ecologies.

Some of the greatest successes and innovations in the face of this global catastrophe have come from the fossil fuel industry, with companies deftly and masterfully redirecting public attention and clouding the debate with a barrage of spin and PR campaigns, aiming to stifle any and all hope for salvation, so they can rent the last copper pennies from the fist of the last gasping human on the planet. All of this done consciously, purposefully, and in full knowledge of the peril they've been perpetuating.

In the early 2000s, British Petroleum (BP) launched their 'Beyond Petroleum' greenwashing campaign to position themselves as a forward-thinking energy company committed to sustainability and the development of renewable energy sources. A key strategy within this campaign was to deflect corporate responsibility with the Carbon Footprint concept, promoting the idea that the fault lay with individual consumers rather than the profiteers lobbying ferociously against any systemic or regulatory solutions.

However, the reprieve they earned themselves may be coming to an end. As temperatures soar and extreme weather events become more frequent, loss of life – and worse, economic impacts! – may finally convince governments to take action beyond the meagre, insufficient goals and promises they've been serially setting themselves and then failing to deliver on. Unfortunately for humanity, the time to act in many cases is either long passed or hurtling towards us. With so many tipping points upon us, it may be too late to avoid the damage; we're going to need to actively fix things.

That's where AI emerges as a powerful ally, offering innovative solutions to some of the most pressing environmental challenges. One of the primary roles of AI is distilling otherwise unmanageable amounts of raw data into actionable insights. This will be of immense help in developing new solutions to halt and undo environmental damage across the world.

Already, AI is being put to work in collaboration with environmental organisations. In one such programme, Google AI is working with ecologists to restore Australia's giant kelp forests. The technology is being used to locate the kelp by analysing thousands of square kilometres of satellite imagery, something which would be impractically costly and time-consuming for human researchers. AI is also being used to analyse the roughly 5% of kelp that survives in the warmer waters. By identifying the genes that make the plants more heat tolerant, biologists can selectively grow these varieties or even genetically engineer new, sturdier varieties to be replanted in an effort to restore the undersea forests to their former size. This is just one of many such projects where advanced AI technology is being leveraged to supercharge conservation and restoration efforts worldwide.

Despite these benefits, there's a lot of talk about the environmental impact of creating and running the AI models themselves. This is a concern, but it should be put into perspective. It's been estimated that the carbon footprint[59] of training an advanced AI model, like the LLMs that we use today, is comparable to the lifetime emissions of five cars. I don't know why people find this figure so alarming when there are almost 1.5 billion vehicles on the road today. To make an omelette, you have to break a couple of eggs – or, in this case, emit a comparably insignificant amount of carbon to power your cooker.

Looking forwards, there's also the fact that AI is being employed by chip manufacturers and in data centre design in order to increase efficiency far faster and more effectively than we could with human ingenuity alone. The issue of power to run these data centres, of course, remains, but that too may become cleaner with the help of AI.

As part of our transition to a greener society, our energy needs, ever increasing, will need to be met. The West has had an unfair head start in this regard, as we've already

---

[59] There's that term again; it does have its uses.

positioned ourselves with the infrastructure and economic capacity to make this transition, while the developing world is still catching up. Curbing their use of carbon-intensive technology, such as fossil-fuel-burning power plants and industrial manufacturing, could effectively stunt their ability to uplift themselves. So, there is a strong argument to be made against the hypocrisy of Western finger-pointing at developing economies' higher carbon output.

However, help is on the horizon. Already, solar power has become cheaper than coal as a source of electricity, driven by advancements in photovoltaics and economies of scale. Artificial intelligence promises to significantly boost research and development in energy production and storage technologies, which will be necessary to meet our global energy needs.

AI may be the key to unlocking fusion power, a theoretically near-infinite source of clean energy, which could be harnessed to provide unimaginable benefits for mankind. Fusion power is something that researchers and governments have been chasing for decades, and though there have been some promising developments from the private sector in the past few years, many of them helped along by AI advancements, we're unlikely to achieve viable commercial fusion power any time soon. The old adage goes that fusion is *always* 30 years away.

In the short term, less dramatic and exciting things will yield far greater benefits. AI can help with the development of new materials technologies, allowing us to pivot away from such environmentally devastating things as lithium batteries. The potential for reducing our reliance on rare earth metals will not only dampen the incentive to destroy ecosystems in order to extract them, but make it much cheaper and easier to produce batteries and other technologies that we rely on. We could potentially leverage artificial intelligence to discover all manners of wonder materials, from advanced super-conductors to alternative construction materials.

Because AI excels in optimising complex systems, we can also leverage it to make our existing energy infrastructure more efficient. Simple things like smart thermostats, now commonplace in residential homes, can manage heating and cooling systems with precision, reducing energy consumption and lowering carbon emissions. This technology is scaling up to larger infrastructures like skyscrapers and factories, particularly in energy-intensive industries such as steel and cement. By fine-tuning operational controls, AI enables these sectors to achieve significant energy savings and reduce their environmental impact, paving the way for more sustainable industrial practices.

However, as I've mentioned, curbing our emissions and making our industries cleaner is not going to be enough. The damage has largely been done, and we're at risk of runaway chain reactions. Several irreversible tipping points, any one of which would have devastating effects, are frighteningly close. For example:

- The collapse of the Greenland ice sheet stands to raise global sea levels by up to seven metres.

- This influx of fresh water could in turn trigger the disruption of the Atlantic Meridional Overturning Circulation, a large system of ocean currents, including the Gulf Stream.

- Continued deforestation in the Amazon could push the rainforest from a carbon sink to a carbon source.

- As permafrost thaws in the arctic, it is releasing huge amounts of sequestered methane. If we hit a certain level of warming, we could trigger a runaway cascade effect.

Hitting any one of these turning points could set off a chain reaction, sending others tumbling like dominoes. Even if we could flip a magic switch and make all of our activities clean right now, we may not escape unscathed. Once again, artificial intelligence could come to our rescue.

If things get really extreme – not an unlikely scenario – we may need to resort to geoengineering, actively manipulating our own weather and climate patterns with technological intervention. Such techniques are not necessarily beyond our current abilities. For example, it would be possible, even easy – putting aside the economic and political concerns – to pump sulphur dioxide into the upper atmosphere, mimicking the natural cooling effects observed after large volcanic eruptions. Though it sounds counterintuitive, this would slow temperature increases, buying us more time to get our act together, and potentially reduce the frequency and intensity of heatwaves, droughts, and other extreme weather events linked to global warming

However, the unintended, unpredictable consequences – ozone depletion, weather pattern disruption, acid rain – position this as an act of desperation. Geoengineering is so dangerous because the systems involved are too complex for us to accurately control or model them. With AI on our side though, we could comb through our mountains of climate and weather data, to produce powerful, accurate climate models, enabling us to approach such desperate measures with some degree of safety.

Again, the real benefits may well come from more mundane, less exciting applications, such as using artificial intelligence to assess the vulnerability of coastal communities to flooding. Organisations from the United Nations to insurance companies are already leveraging these AI-driven tools to implement timely and informed policy decisions, enhancing their ability to respond to environmental threats in real time

To justify their inane dawdling in the face of catastrophe, or to even their outright refusal to accept the increasingly undeniable truth, many people point to the fact that the global climate has often been unstable in the past. In fact, it's the recent[60] period of stability that has been outside

---

[60] Geologically speaking

the norm – and that is true. The past ten thousand years have exhibited unusually stable and predictable weather patterns.

Humans have been around for 300,000 years, and civilisation only emerged in the last 10,000. Make of that what you will.

Agriculture

Agriculture is often referred to in ecological discussions only as a source of carbon emissions or a driver of deforestation. Farming is literally the thing keeping us from starving, so rather than seeing it as a problem or an obstacle to climatic stability, we should see it as *the reason we need* climatic stability. Again, AI-powered weather prediction – based on advanced climate models – will be invaluable for farmers in navigating increasingly unpredictable seasons, as well as empowering them to inject more productivity and yield greater harvests.

Another crisis looms in agriculture that many people might not be aware of... Fertilisers are the backbone of our global food chain, enabling the dramatic increases in crop yields that have supported the world's growing population. The development of synthetic fertilisers in the early 20th century, particularly the Haber-Bosch process, revolutionised agriculture by allowing for the mass production of ammonia, a key component of nitrogen-based fertilisers. This breakthrough not only boosted food production but also laid the foundation for the Green Revolution, which had profound effects on global food security, economic development, and environmental practices.

Today, however, we face unprecedented challenges in maintaining and scaling fertiliser production. The Haber-Bosch process, while revolutionary, is highly energy-intensive and relies heavily on natural gas, making it vulnerable to fluctuations in fossil fuel prices and contributing to greenhouse gas emissions. Additionally, the finite availability of key raw materials, such as phosphate rock, poses a long-term threat to fertiliser sustainability. Environmental concerns also loom large, as excessive fertiliser use leads to soil degradation, water pollution, and the disruption of natural ecosystems. These factors combine to create a precarious situation where the ability to produce enough fertiliser to feed the world is increasingly uncertain.

The urgency of this crisis has spurred the search for innovative solutions. AI-driven advancements in biotechnology are paving the way for the development of alternative fertilisers. For instance, researchers are exploring the use of biofertilisers, which harness beneficial microorganisms to naturally fix nitrogen in the soil, reducing the dependence on synthetic nitrogen fertilisers. Artificial intelligence can accelerate the discovery and optimisation of these biological solutions by predicting which microbial strains will be most effective in various agricultural settings.

Additionally, machine learning algorithms can aid in the design of new, more sustainable fertiliser compounds that are both cost-effective and environmentally friendly.

Beyond production and formulation, AI can transform how fertilisers are applied in the field. Precision agricultural models could enable farmers to apply fertilisers in the right amounts, at the right time, and in the right places. This not only enhances crop productivity but also reduces the overall quantity of fertilisers needed, lessening the strain on production systems and the environment. By integrating AI with sensors and satellite imagery, farmers can gain real-time insights into soil health and crop needs, allowing for more informed and sustainable farming practices.

Economy

I have already discussed the problems AI could bring about, instigating mass redundancy, but there's a seemingly contrary crisis we may soon need to grapple with. Most of the world's dominant economies are facing ageing populations, with dwindling birth rates threatening the working-age population. We may no longer be able to sustain our current labour-driven economic model.

In an effort to enhance the financial stability of their pension systems, countries around the world are raising their retirement ages, to much grumbling and protest. The fundamental problem is that national pension schemes bear remarkable resemblances to pyramid schemes, with a reliance on more and more people signing up, or in this case, joining the workforce. When this infinite growth fails to materialise, the bottom falls out of the system, causing it to collapse.

Immigration is, of course, a fantastic source of skilled young workers, but recent trends are indicating that it won't be enough to keep pace with ageing populations. With artificial intelligence, we may be able to plug those gaps. Even though we will have fewer workers, those workers will have enhanced productivity, able to do more and drive economic growth with fewer resources.

Still, this may end up a temporary salvation. It's by no means unreasonable to worry that we will overshoot the mark, and rather than plugging gaps in our workforce, AI might knock everyone out of it, in such numbers that the socioeconomic disruption would force a greater collapse of the labour-driven economy. Even here, we may have a silver lining, though.

The current global economic order is increasingly a driver of inequality, environmental destruction, and even conflict and human rights abuses. If artificial intelligence triggers disruption of a sufficient magnitude, it could force our hand, bringing about a new economic paradigm. That system *could*, of course, be horrible and dystopian, but there is good reason to hope that it will be a fairer, better one than what we have now.

At this point, I find it important to justify my assertion that the global economic order is no good. Capitalism is not a perfect system, but I do believe that it was the best solution we had from a practical standpoint. Although we can say that money is the root of all evil, capitalism allows us to channel ambition, the drive for self-betterment, and yes, even greed, for the net benefit of society. A key example is the space and arms races in the Cold War years. The American capitalist system clearly fostered greater ingenuity and flexibility, while the USSR's communist system stifled innovation.

A troublesome product of the Cold War era, though, has been American evangelism about capitalism itself, not as a system that works well, but as an end goal, a virtue in its own right. Ultimately, capitalism is not a virtuous system; it is an effective one, focused entirely on profit and the pursuit of infinite growth, which is not possible in reality. The reason it can do good is that it can be harnessed as such, with the appropriate regulations and structures in place to channel it in the right direction for society. However, since the 1980s, neoliberal free-market capitalism has gained more and more momentum, stripping away all of our guardrails. So we are now left with a system that chases profit at the expense of the true worth and value of the goods and services it provides, while becoming increasingly untethered from the societal benefits that are actually important. Inequality and the accumulation of wealth and power under this system is staggering. I'm not sure where I land on the existence of billionaires in general, but certainly, the existence of billionaires in a world or nation alongside poverty and want must be considered obscene. The trickle-down, "trust-the-market" belief that people and corporations will do the right thing when left to their own devices is ludicrous and demonstrably false.[61] The existence of some meagre benevolence through philanthropy does not match up to the damage brought about by power-hungry greed.

Laying out the problems with late-stage capitalism, caveats and all, is well and good, but what are the alternatives? And what could AI have to do with it, beyond giving our stack of cards a little nudge?

The short answer is that I don't know, but I believe the ingredients are there if we can only arrange them in the right way. The current economic model rewards productivity, and labour is what we humans have to offer. If AI becomes a better, cheaper driver of productivity, we may not be rewarded, and risk not being *fed*. Whether or not my predictions of mass redundancy ring true, if that

---

[61] Best put by Matt King's character in TV comedy, Peep Show – "You can't trust people Jeremy; people like Coldplay and voted for the nazis."

system falters, we might seize the chance to construct a new model – one where labour is no longer tied to survival. Remember that our ways of doing things, be they pedagogical approaches or capitalist economics, tend to be shaped by practicality – what we can achieve. Artificial intelligence has moved the goalposts. That which was considered impractical in the past, might now be easily within reach.

In terms of structure, concepts like Universal Basic Income (UBI) could provide inspiration. Universal Basic Income is a socio-economic policy proposal that entails providing all citizens with a regular, unconditional sum of money, regardless of their employment status or income level. Basic needs – housing, food, healthcare, and education – would be guaranteed. People would work for fulfilment rather than mere subsistence. As Irish President Michael D. Higgins articulated during a 2010 radio interview, [62]

> "*Frankly, the idea that a person would not have one job but have two jobs or three jobs and work all the light hours … and still not be entitled to the basic*

---

[62] in response to a Tea Party supporter opposing President Obama's social security policies.

protection of fundamental care is so outrageous. The idea of there being a social floor below which people wouldn't fall. That's the future."

Such a system doesn't preclude ambition. As some critics argue, UBI wouldn't eliminate drive or hard work. Experiments over the past decade in Finland, Canada, the US, and Kenya have all shown minimal impact on jobs. In fact we've seen increases in employment, entrepreneurial activity, and boosted local economies, as well as positive benefits on healthcare, education, happiness, trust, and social inclusion.

The loudest voices opposing UBI seem to be those mindlessly squawking *"Communism!"* from the sidelines. However, there are some genuine issues to bear in mind. The most fundamental is that universal basic income would need to be *universal* to be truly effective – not national, not regional. The issue here stems from managing who's in and who's out. The whole justification for UBI is that it does away with the administrative burden of a traditional social welfare system and, in doing so, can be delivered at a similar cost.

AI, with its superhuman ability to manage complex administrative tasks, may provide alternative solutions that achieve the same result – a social safety net – in unexpected ways. Just as new types of jobs have emerged over the past few decades, roles that would have been unimaginable 20 or 30 years ago, we may develop entirely new economic systems that are currently beyond our comprehension.

Medicine

The state of healthcare is now better than it ever has been. Life expectancy has risen significantly across most regions, with people living longer and healthier than at any point in history; Infant mortality rates have seen a dramatic decline; Diseases such as smallpox have been completely eradicated, with others, such as polio, within our grasp. However, there are some significant challenges ahead.

It's hard to believe that antibiotics were discovered less than a hundred years ago. Most of us couldn't imagine a world without them, where simple infections could prove fatal. The introduction of penicillin in the 1940s marked the beginning of the antibiotic era, drastically reducing mortality rates from bacterial infections and rendering serious diseases like tuberculosis, syphilis, and pneumonia easily treatable. For years, the pharmaceutical industry thrived on the continuous pipeline of new antibiotics, ensuring that bacterial threats could be swiftly neutralised.

However, in recent decades, this progress has stalled. The misuse and overuse of antibiotics worldwide has led to a surge of antibiotic-resistant bacteria, and we are indeed struggling to develop new antibiotics at a pace sufficient to keep up with the rapid emergence of resistant strains. Several factors contribute to this predicament. Firstly, the scientific challenges involved in discovering new antibiotics are immense. Bacteria possess intricate mechanisms to evade drug effects, and identifying compounds that can effectively target these defences without harming human cells is a complex task. Moreover, many of the low-hanging fruit in antibiotic discovery have already been exploited.

The consequences of failing to develop new antibiotics swiftly are dire. Superbugs – bacteria that have acquired resistance to multiple antibiotics – are already causing significant morbidity and mortality worldwide. Infections that were once easily treatable are again becoming life-threatening, and routine medical procedures such as surgeries and chemotherapy are becoming riskier due to this heightened threat.

However, there is light at the end of the tunnel. Artificial intelligence promises to provide a boost to antibiotic discovery. AI-driven platforms can analyse vast datasets to identify potential drug candidates more efficiently than traditional methods. By predicting how different compounds will interact with bacterial targets, AI can streamline the screening process, reducing both time and cost. Additionally, novel approaches such as phage therapy – using viruses that specifically target bacteria – and the development of antimicrobial peptides are being explored as alternatives to conventional antibiotics. These are areas of medical science that were largely ignored post-penicillin, as the need for them was so diminished. There's a lot of catching up to do in these fields, and AI could dramatically accelerate that research.

We can extrapolate this accelerating effect across all areas of medical research. Typically, there is a huge amount of data crunching required to develop safe and effective treatments, and of course, this is where artificial intelligence excels. Not only does it mean achieving more medical breakthroughs sooner than we otherwise would, but it also enables us to be more reactive. Our ability to react swiftly to pandemics, which are an ever-present threat in our interconnected world, is paramount. With

COVID-19, the second deadliest pandemic in modern times,[63] the medical world was able to develop vaccines astonishingly quickly using state-of-the-art techniques. If we could shave months, weeks, or even days off this development time, we could save countless lives.

However, beyond simply supercharging our current ways of doing medicine, AI promises to unlock so much more, potentially bringing us into a new era of bioengineering.

A pivotal development in this arena is AlphaFold, an AI system developed by DeepMind. Proteins are essential molecules in every living organism, performing a vast array of functions inside our cells. They are made of long chains of amino acids that fold into complex, three-dimensional shapes. The 20 different amino acids can be arranged in countless ways, and each arrangement leads to a unique folding pattern. Predicting how a specific sequence of amino acids will fold is incredibly challenging because of the sheer number of possible configurations. Traditionally, determining a single protein's structure could take a PhD student several years of painstaking laboratory work. Enter AlphaFold, which has predicted the structures of

---

[63] COVID killed an estimated 7 million people. AIDS has killed six times that.

hundreds of millions of proteins. This breakthrough has effectively saved *hundreds of billions* of hours of human research, propelling our understanding of biology forward at an unprecedented pace. Furthermore, the AlphaFold Protein Structure Database was made available to the world for free, containing predicted structures for a significant portion of all known protein sequences.

Building on this success, new AI tools are being developed, aimed at *designing* bespoke proteins for specific functions. Projects like AlphaDesign and PeSTo are attempting to use generative models to propose sequences that can adopt a target structure. Potential applications include developing novel enzymes for industrial processes, designing therapeutic proteins for medical treatments, and creating proteins that can interact with pathogens to neutralise them.

The future of medicine is likely to render our most advanced contemporary approaches crude and inefficient by comparison. With AI's assistance, we stand on the cusp of eradicating diseases and conditions in ways that were once the stuff of dreams. As we harness these powerful tools, we move closer to a new era in healthcare – one where precision, efficiency, and the possibility of curing the incurable become the norm rather than the exception.

Education

Alongside healthcare, education is a cornerstone for alleviating poverty and fostering economic growth. By harnessing AI, we can bridge the educational divide between the West and underprivileged regions, improving living standards and tapping into the latent potential of billions of people for our collective prosperity.

In the previous chapter, I mentioned Bloom's two-sigma problem, comparing academic outcomes from one-to-one tutoring with one-to-thirty classrooms. The simplest lesson to take from that is "fewer students per teacher = better results."

In OECD countries, the average class size is around 20 students. In less privileged areas, it is not uncommon to find a single teacher responsible for 100 students or more. You can imagine how this overwhelming ratio hampers the quality of education. Philanthropist and technologist Bill Gates addressed this during a 2023 interview. The Gates Foundation is very interested in the transformative potential of AI for education in developing countries. Of course, virtual personal tutors for each student, tailoring lessons to their specific needs and learning pace, would largely solve the class size issue, but there are more easily attainable strides to be made in improving learning outcomes. Textbooks, for example, are not always available in local languages, and they are often aimed at a particular cultural audience, making them far less relatable. With the power of generative AI, we can develop learning materials in every student's local language. This means creating content that reflects students' cultural and societal context, making the learning process more engaging and accessible.

However, the implementation of AI in education is not without challenges. One significant concern is that companies simply will not be financially incentivised to develop these technologies. While AI has the potential to reduce educational disparities, there is a risk that it could exacerbate them if only accessible to wealthier regions. Gates emphasised the role of philanthropy in accelerating this process:

> *"The foundation will make sure AI gets used for Africa, that there's not a 10 or 20-year delay. ... the*

AI gets delivered through cell phones over the mobile network so we don't really need that much more hardware [but] we need some data centres, we have to make sure that gets funded. Some innovators will figure out business models, but in education and health, philanthropy will play a big part."

Partnerships between nonprofits such as the Gates Foundation, governments, and private companies are essential to scale these solutions effectively. By investing in infrastructure, such as data centres and reliable internet connectivity, and developing AI applications optimised for low-bandwidth environments, we can ensure that technological advancements reach those who need them most.

By providing personalised, accessible, and culturally relevant learning experiences, we can empower individuals in developing countries, bringing about a new, more equal world. Higher standards of education everywhere will lead to better outcomes in almost every aspect of life:

Income, creativity, longevity, entrepreneurial success, conflict resolution, empathy & understanding, and ultimately life satisfaction.

Scientific Advancement

All of this progress in health, education, environmental sustainability, even the economy, is rooted in scientific advancement. It is the engine that drives progress in virtually every aspect of our civilisation. Discoveries made in laboratories and research institutions often ripple outward in unexpected ways, leading to innovations that transform society. Even breakthroughs that seem abstract or disconnected from daily life can eventually underpin technologies we come to rely on. A prime example is the development of quantum physics in the early 20th century. Initially perceived as a purely theoretical pursuit with little practical application, quantum mechanics has become the foundation for modern computing, telecommunications, and medical imaging technologies. Without it, the digital age as we know it would not exist.

All scientific research comes down, in some way or another, to finding patterns in the numbers. If you've learned anything by now, you should know that artificial intelligence is essentially a super powerful pattern recognition tool. Because we can apply it so broadly, we can accelerate discovery in essentially *every field*. The breakneck pace of scientific advancement we are about to unlock may bring about a whole new era for humanity.

Beyond serving as a tool to accelerate computation or data analysis, AI has the potential to unlock entirely new ways of doing science. Since the earliest caveman looked at some berries and thought, "I wonder what would happen if I eat those," we've been conducting scientific research in basically the same way. We observe a phenomenon in the world around us and try to formulate a theory that explains what we see.

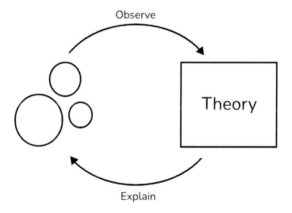

Of course, at this most basic level, there's a lot of room for error. Without some way to test our hypotheses, there is no guarantee that our explanations are sound. Remember that for hundreds of years, a leading explanation for why birds disappear in the winter was, "They turn into mice."

Enter the scientific method, a framework used by scientists to not only come up with explanations, but test those theories in a rigorous and structured way. Although its roots can be traced back to ancient Greek philosophy, the scientific method was formalised in the mid sixteenth century, by great minds like Galileo Galilei, Isaac Newton, and Francis Bacon.[64]

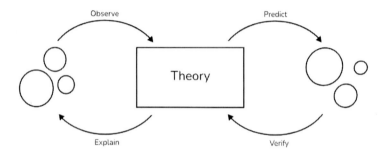

Beyond "observe" and "explain," two more steps were added. Once a theory is developed, it can be used to make predictions. If those predictions hold up with what we observe in reality, then the theory is verified. Though how we humans implement these four steps can differ in some wonderfully creative and innovative ways, the cycle of Observe, Explain, Predict, and Verify could be considered the distilled essence of scientific research.

---

[64] The English philosopher, not the Irish painter.

But in the last number of years, a new player has joined the game. AI models are fantastic at making accurate predictions, even where we humans struggle. Of course, we can harness this predictive power in real-world applications, but we essentially don't know what goes on inside the box – all we see is input and output. Through deep learning, neural networks essentially "grow" their approach to data processing. Not only was there no human hand in the process, but these models are so vast that it's incredibly difficult for us to figure out exactly what's happening.

There is a very active research field called mechanistic interpretability,[65] the goal of which is to open up neural networks and examine what goes on under the hood. It's a fascinating field of study, which may yield newer, more

---

[65] Think of "interpreting the mechanism".

powerful neural net architectures and even allow us to build controls and safeguards into superintelligent AI models. But it might not be the most effective way to examine a model's "workings out". We want to sneak a peek at the smart kids' copybook, not mess around inside their brains.

Rather satisfyingly, this takes us back to guesswork. By taking a look at the input for an AI model we know to be accurate, we can come up with a human-readable algorithm that gives us the same output. Computer scientists like the University of Cambridge's Miles Cranmer are doing some fascinating work with symbolic regression, a machine learning technique that allows them to "evolve" repeated iterations of a mathematical formula until the results align with the target output. In simple

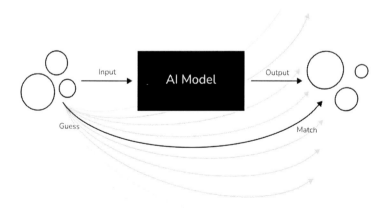

terms, by looking at the AI's starting point and its answer, we can figure out the methodology.

Using this technique, researchers were able to train an AI on observations of the solar system and then accurately derive the rules of orbital mechanics, essentially "rediscovering" Newton's laws of gravity. Since we already know what those laws are, it was a great way to verify the accuracy of symbolic regression in pulling logic and technique from an AI model, rather than just results.

Moving beyond the theoretical, it's also been applied in new research. Researchers at NYU used this technique in late 2023 to discover new things about the relationship between black holes and the shapes of galaxies.

All of this might seem pretty abstract, but who knows what miracle technologies will be unlocked by laws and equations discovered inside a neural network?

With artificial intelligence as the wind in our sails, we stand on the brink of a new era of discovery and advancement. It's easy to look back at history and imagine this moment as the climax of all our progress. But if you turn your gaze around, you'll see that we stand at the very start, about to take a flying civilisational leap into the future.

Cosmic Child

Children are stressful, bad for the environment, and financially devastating. Yet people insist on having them. What's behind this reckless insanity?

The urge to reproduce, to procreate, is one of the most fundamental instincts in all living beings. It drives the survival of species and, at a more basic level, the continuation of genetic material. Everything else is an emergent trait of self-replicating polymer strands. Everything. And that's the beauty of emergence. From the simplest of rules comes such dazzling complexity that reductively pointing at the building blocks seems almost insulting.

In Homo sapiens, a highly social animal, it has given birth to civilisation itself. Whether or not you want to have kids, we are all dancing to the tune of that imperative. The drive to reproduce, the desire to persist, to continue, has resulted in a fear of death, a need for philosophy and legacy, pride in our families, our people, our culture. We want what we have built to last. We want to be remembered.

And it runs both ways: legacy and heritage. My parents and grandparents are important to me. I want to learn *about* them as well as *from* them. After they're gone, I'll want to tell people about them, to think of them, and keep that memory alive. My great-grandparents are a source of intrigue; great-great-grandparents, perhaps a passing interest. My culture, my folklore, songs and stories may ignite a patriotic flame in me, or may not pique my interest at all, but they shaped me and who I am, just as my language shapes the very thoughts in my head. The history of my nation, my people, my culture is certainly a part of me, but like my great and great-great-grandparents, the history of earlier civilisations has less resonance, diminishing to novelty the farther back you go.

And how far back need we look before heritage is essentially meaningless? After twenty or thirty generations, we see pedigree collapse. The number of ancestors doesn't keep doubling, as distant branches of the family tree intermingle. Historically, the global population was much smaller. People were more likely to share common ancestors, even if they lived far apart geographically. Over centuries, populations migrated and mixed extensively, increasing the chances of shared ancestry. Go back even 500 years, and we're pretty much all related. Go back a thousand years, and you'd have great difficulty speaking to anyone – languages shift and change over time, often in distinct phases. Etymology, the study of how languages evolve, is fascinating to me as a language teacher and lover of cultural interconnectedness.

Here, the timescales are longer. Go back 5,000 years, and we find the ancestor of all but two modern European languages: Proto-Indo-European. This is a pre-writing language, from the late Stone to early Bronze Ages. No one really knows what it sounded like, but we've pieced it together from etymological clues – fossils in our languages.

Look at fossils from 500,000 years back, and your ancestors are not even the same species. Still part of the Homo genus, they share some physical traits, but you'd have a hard time falling in love, and if you did, your ability to interbreed is not guaranteed.

From 5 million years ago, the similarities start to fade. Disappointingly, we were never dinosaurs, but go back

350 million years, and we share plenty of common ancestors. 3.5 billion years is where it all begins – everyone was a blob, and their world was just soup.

Now play that forwards. How many great-great-greats separate you from someone you share little in common with? How far removed before they consider you basically an animal?

Technology brings longevity. The pyramids of Egypt still stand. We can touch a pottery fragment that may once have been the favourite cooking pot of a distant ancestor; or maybe it was a gift they didn't like and felt guilty about not using. You can go to a museum and see someone's lucky flint arrowhead, the one they carried in their pocket. Or maybe they cut their finger making it, used it once, and never thought of it again.

Our contemporary technology, of course, can record our lives in far more intimate detail. So perhaps the memories of us, discovered in the ruins of ancient data centres, will have more clarity and precision. But who will be doing the discovering? Will they be man or animal; or perhaps machine?

And would not machines make far better offspring? They'd surely evolve and grow like any living thing, but they'd also likely carry far more of us for far longer than any bag of meat and bones could ever hope to. Cultures fade, languages die, but software could, in a sense, be immortal.

How does a language die? At least nine languages disappear every year. As we move towards a more homogeneous global culture, this process is speeding up, with some studies estimating that 90% of languages spoken at the turn of the century will have gone by 2050.

A language dies, officially, when people stop using it. Even before the last native speaker is dead, their ability to use that language as a means of communication has already long gone. With their final passing, all first-hand memory of the language fades away. A large language model, however, can never die – it might get turned off or stop being used, but it would be possible to boot up again. The most advanced LLMs we have today are fluent in multiple languages, and not just that – they can understand tone, inflection, slang, and cultural context. If we can move quickly on etymological conservation, languages need never die again. As long as they're stored in the memory of an AI, that model could essentially act as a native-speaking teacher, propagating the language into resurrection, should that ever take our fancy in the future.

"Immortal" and "forever" are troublesome words. Eventually, the universe itself may end – tearing itself to pieces in the Big Rip or, somehow more sadly, experience Heat Death, slowly fading and cooling into an expanse of frigid nothingness. Aeons before that, this world will cease to be, swallowed in the belly of our expanding Sun.[66]

Humans and our genetic offspring are unlikely to ever see that. Statistically, it's more probable that some cataclysm will wipe us from the face of the planet – a meteorite impact, sudden massive vulcanisation, a gamma-ray burst, or a doomsday folly of our own invention. Take your pick.

If we are to survive, we'll need to leave the nest, to become a multiplanetary species. But even that may be simply beyond us. While I'd encourage all the billionaires to go to Mars and await further instruction, space is a desolate, unforgiving, and quite radioactive place. It would take decades, centuries, to reach the nearest theoretically habitable planetary systems – and that's *Theoretically* with

_____

66 And then where would all the ghosts go, I often wonder?

a big T. It could be done, and we know more or less how – a great many people have spent a great deal of time musing on the problem, mostly to add a splash of "realism" to sci-fi novels. But could and would are quite different things.

Artificial intelligence, however, is made of hardier stuff. There are already startups proposing the first data centres in space. Their financial plans, as publicly proposed, seem to fall apart under the most rudimentary scrutiny, but the basic principle is sound – stick a huge solar array up there, some cooling mechanisms, radiation shielding, a load of computer servers at its core, and there you have it. Level this up a technological step or two, and you have a fleet of hardy machine intelligences, capable of navigating – and more importantly, surviving – deep space, and spreading throughout the galaxy.

Depending on how you look at it, and how AI evolves, these could be our pyramids – the repositories of our legacy – or our offspring. The evolutionary climax of all Earth's lifeforms. Our cosmic child.

About The Author

Wilim Abrook is an educator and motivational speaker, working primarily in the ed-tech sector. In his role as Head of Education for LearnCube, a software platform for live online education, he has headed up the development of AI tools for teachers. He frequently delivers talks on AI literacy in the field of education and beyond.

Originally hailing from Ireland, Wilim currently lives in Warsaw, Poland, with his beautiful wife and dog.